Little Doubt

LITTLE DOUBT

RACHEL LYNCH

CANELO

First published in the United Kingdom in 2020 by

Canelo Digital Publishing Limited
Third Floor, 20 Mortimer Street
London W1T 3JW
United Kingdom

A CIP catalogue record for this book is available from the British Library.

Print ISBN 978 1 78863 789 3
Ebook ISBN 978 1 78863 756 5

Look for more great books at www.canelo.co

Printed and bound in Great Britain by Clays Ltd, Elcograf S.p.A.

Chapter 1

Ella Watson filled the drum of the washing machine to bursting. It was her least favourite chore and she stuffed the items in roughly. There wasn't even space for a tea towel. School PE kit, stuff picked up off the floor of teenagers' bedrooms, as well as golfing, hiking and skiing paraphernalia for their holiday made the machine groan. She had a hundred and one things to get done, and she liked to be ahead of schedule when planning for their holidays. They were to spend Christmas in their chalet in Val Thorens, and she'd got everything out of the loft to wash. It wasn't actually a chalet, more of a penthouse, but one mustn't boast.

Despite her list of mounting errands, she was still determined to go for a run.

Their house was set back from Ullswater, on the south shore, hidden away behind a wall of rhododendrons and an electric iron gate. From the sitting room on the first floor, the lake could be viewed in its full majesty, and Ella paused as she went through the room to her bedroom upstairs. Beyond the lake, she could consider the fells that painted the background to the view, and soak up the tranquillity. Winter was well on its way. The light was beautiful today, she observed. The ancient trees on the north shore were a mixture of various hues of orange, grey and green. But the warmth of the landscape belied the freezing temperatures. Going to her room, she wrapped up in two thermal layers and her warmest running trousers. Her running gloves were downstairs. She might even take a hat.

She rarely went in to Penrith – it was fairly grotty, except for the castle – but today she had to visit the Apple Store because her son, Jordan, had dropped his phone again. She insisted on taking it to an official outlet to replace the broken screen, rather than a corner shop promising deals. Her plan was to pop in and leave the phone, then try out Potton Park for a jog. She'd never run there before, but she thought it looked pretty. It was close to the centre of Penrith and a nod to rural charm and clean air.

The house was quiet as she gathered her things for the morning ahead. Thomas, her husband, was on the golf course. She knew she was lucky, but then they'd earned their privileges. Thomas had done stints in Manchester and London and given his pound of flesh to corporatism. Now, at fifty, it was their time to enjoy the fruits of their labour, away from the big cities. They'd lived near Ullswater for three years.

As she left the house, her breath escaped in vapour clouds. There must have been a frost last night, she thought. She opened the garage and unlocked her Range Rover Sport, throwing her running bag, gloves and hat on the passenger seat. She'd wear a jacket to go into town. The garage closed automatically as she pulled away and headed along the shore of the lake, passing walkers heading out to the fells, swaddled in layers of thermal kit. Their faces looked ruddy and fresh. Her favourite season in the Lakes was spring, when life burst through the hard ground and announced itself in swathes of colour, but autumn came a close second. The dark nights, sitting in front of an open fire preparing for Christmas with the kids, and fewer tourists all made it feel less crazy than the summer.

After her run, she needed to do some shopping in Keswick, but she planned to have everything done in time to get home and take her son to football. Jordan was a sports addict, while her daughter, Millie, hated any kind of physical activity – except skiing – preferring piano and Spanish. The children attended a private school on the outskirts of Keswick. At sixteen and fourteen, they were almost – but not quite – old enough to be left alone in the house overnight. She'd discussed with Thomas the idea of stealing away for a dirty weekend somewhere and decided that they'd perhaps try it next year. If it proved to be a success, and they didn't come back to the detritus and carnage of a teenage party, they'd even go abroad.

The clear blue sky reminded her of her wedding day. They'd married in November, and everyone had said she should wear fur, but the sky had been just like today: bright blue and clear. It would be their twentieth anniversary next week, and Thomas had bought her a spectacular ruby ring, which they'd chosen together. It probably wasn't a piece to wear daily, but Ella couldn't help herself, and she admired it affectionately as she tapped the steering wheel. They'd insured it for ten thousand pounds. It was a whole band of the claret stones, in an intricate medieval-style setting.

She came to the little hamlet of Pooley Bridge, where the traffic grew thick and two worlds collided jarringly. The south shore of Ullswater apart from campsites and rugged hills, was largely a haven of peace and quiet. As she hit the main road to Penrith, however, her spirits sagged a little: the sky seemed less bright, and clouds hung over the buildings in the distance. The town was large and noisy, and confirmed why she didn't go there often, though the red sandstone of the oldest structures was attractive. In the distance, the silhouettes of estates and high-rises provided a drab backdrop. The centre itself comprised a mixture of trendy chains, eateries and pubs, competing with bargain-basement outlets and bankrupt boutiques. Ella didn't associate with anyone in the town: their paths simply didn't cross. If she and Thomas fancied a quality meal in a restaurant, they'd go to a smart hotel on one of the lakes, or down to Cartmel to the two-Michelin-starred L'Enclume.

She parked in one of the large pay-and-displays and took her jacket from the back seat. She locked up as she walked briskly away, bracing herself against a piercing wind. The high street wasn't far, and she looked forward to going inside a shop to warm up. As she rushed through a shortcut alley, she was distracted by a couple of teenagers who she thought should be at school and bumped straight into a man coming the other way. He was tall and strong and she bounced right off him and into the wall along the side of the narrow alleyway, banging her elbow hard.

'Oh my goodness, are you all right? I'm so sorry,' he said.

Ella gathered herself and smiled.

'It's my fault, I wasn't paying attention. Yes, I'm all right, thank you.'

She carried on along the alley, rubbing her elbow. Calm down, Ella, she told herself.

The trip to the Apple Store only took ten minutes, and she was back at the car in no time at all. She noticed two boys wearing hoodies (she hated Jordan wearing the damn things) smoking cigarettes by the pay-and-display machine, and she scrunched up her nose as the smell wafted in through her open door. She slammed it shut and the boys looked around, sizing up the car and making lewd gestures. Ella was gobsmacked and for a minute didn't know how to react. She started the engine to pull away, but before she could control herself, she flicked an emphatic middle finger at both of them. Unfortunately, her finger was still raised when she rounded the parked cars, and an elderly man stopped dead in his tracks, mouth open, bemused by what he saw. She quickly dropped her hand and mouthed an apology, but it was too late: the old man looked traumatised. She squirmed in shame as the boys fell about laughing.

Potton Park was a popular family venue for young mothers to take prams and picnics, and it was for the most part open and pretty. Ella parked easily beneath a series of huge pines and got out. The wind had died down and she left her gloves and hat in the car. She stretched a little to warm her muscles, and fixed her headphones. Running was her sanctuary. Inside her own world, away from children, husband, shopping and cooking, she could listen to her music, wash away tension and feel invigorated by the outdoors. She set her iPhone to record her circuit; she planned on doing a figure of eight around the pond and the summer pool. The pool was really a splash area for tiny children and hers were far too old to enjoy it. It had jets of water that squirted up to surprise toddlers and give tired mums a break. It was actually quite pretty.

As she set off, she could see a group of people in the distance; she realised as she got closer that it was an outdoor exercise class. The trainer shouted instructions and the participants – all women – ran up and down, taking it in turns to shuttle and do press-ups. It looked like fun. The instructor waved at her and she waved back.

She lost sight of them and rounded a corner sheltered by large trees, still smiling from sharing a connection with fellow exercisers. As she ran, she concentrated on the rhythm of her feet.

Suddenly the wind was knocked out of her by a collision. At first, she had no idea what she'd hit. Her headphones had fallen out, and she tried to look around for them, but her legs had collapsed and she found herself on the floor. There was no pain at first, and she was momentarily puzzled: surely something knocking her to the ground would hurt? But then a throbbing, searing agony the likes of which she'd never experienced burned her back, and she found to her horror that she couldn't move. Another blow thudded into her, and she looked up to see two men standing over her. She didn't know them, but their expressions were screwed up in anger and rage, and something else: excitement? They were so young…

She heard them run away, and struggled to breathe. In her mind, she tried to put her hand over where the pain was, but in reality, she couldn't lift it. She saw that she was surrounded by a pool of blood and she quickly realised that it belonged to her; it was coming out of her. She was lying on her side, and her whole body began to shake. Her vision started to blur. Saliva dribbled out of her mouth, and she coughed. The acute stinging turned to a dark ache, and she closed her eyes. She'd been attacked. It was serious.

She forced her eyes open. The blood was dark, hot and sticky. It was everywhere. She began to panic and saw that it was draining from her body in pulses. Gushes that matched her heartbeat, elevated from her exertion.

Thomas. Jordan. Millie.

Oh God. Her face was next to the gritty road and she could smell the concrete.

Someone help. Please. Please.

She heard faint tinny music coming out of her head-phones, which lay a foot away. It was A-ha. Her energy seeped away and her eyes grew too heavy to keep open.

Thomas. Jordan. Millie...

Chapter 2

Detective Inspector Kelly Porter arrived on scene at 2.34 p.m.

Fresh from holiday, she was tanned and bright-eyed: a look that didn't really fit in with a crime scene in Penrith in winter.

The 999 call had come in at just after 1.20, from a fitness trainer in Potton Park leaving his exercise class. The guy had had quite a shock, as the scene was a grisly one. Kelly had driven the short distance from her office in the centre of the town to the popular park, and left her car just short of the police tape. A white tent had been erected over the location and she was given shoe covers and gloves before she entered the area cordoned off by police. She wore a purple Rab jacket over her smart office gear, and a bobble hat tamed her long auburn hair, which was currently tinged with honey thanks to the Florida sunshine. She braced herself against the cold. It was true that the Lake District was beautiful, but weather-wise it was Baltic. They'd had plenty of snow in recent years, and she and her partner, Johnny, had even skied down parts of Helvellyn.

Sailing round the Florida Keys with Johnny had been their joint birthday present to one another. The views now towards the Beacon Estate, which overlooked the park, were a stark contrast. This time two weeks ago, she'd been sipping Miami Sunrise cocktails and watching fishermen land their lunch, relaxed from a beach massage and glowing with life.

Welcome home.

She greeted the forensic team, who were conducting a search of the vicinity. She'd draw up her own crime-scene log, but she also studied what they'd found so far.

Under the tent, a woman was dead. She'd bled out. It must have been quick, judging by the amount of blood, but Kelly knew that for a minute or so, she would have been terrified.

Kelly had already called Ted Wallis, the senior coroner for the north-west. She wanted him to see the victim where she lay. It was a unique crime scene: slain body in a public place in broad daylight. Before she'd even set foot inside the tent, Kelly knew that she had a hell of a case ahead of her. It was virtually unheard of: the slaying of a jogger, mid-afternoon. The fact that the woman was dressed in athletic clothing and headphones were found near the body indicated that she was a runner. It looked like she was taken by surprise, and the first thing Kelly thought of was a professional hit. However, the location and time of day made that possibility either bold or stupid. There were other scenarios to be worked through: robbery, deranged lunatic on the loose, passion. She'd already begun swirling them about her head.

Fortunately, they already had a name. That was a good start. A forensic officer had discovered a bank card in the woman's running wallet and had also made a call from the victim's phone, which had put them in touch with Thomas Watson, of Willow Sands, Ullswater. Yes, Ella

Watson was his wife. Yes, she was due to be in Penrith today…

The poor bastard had been asked to drive home from the golf course, where he'd been playing nine holes with three friends. He hadn't been told why. It might seem callous, but next of kin deserved to be informed face to face when the crime was this terrible.

But then he might already know, because it could have been him who'd ordered the hit. Husbands and wives did nasty things to one another. With execution-style killings, like this one might turn out to be, the family was always a good place to start. Only three per cent of murders were stranger on stranger. The rest knew each other and passion was usually the motive. Sex, money, jealousy… Kelly needed to get to know Ella Watson.

Before she went into the tent, she paused to assess the lines of sight. A quick wander around the closest bushes took her to open grass; the first thing she saw was the pond, then, further away, the high-rises of the Beacon Estate. She looked left and right, and saw that bushes and trees blocked every other pathway, apart from the concrete path that snaked back to the main entrance and the centre of Penrith.

She ducked inside the tent.

The amount of blood was staggering. She paused for a moment to take in the violence of the crime. Ella Watson had yet to be formally identified, but from the link to her husband's phone, plus the bank card, they had little doubt. The tent was particularly large, to cover the blood pool from prying eyes outside. The path's camber sloped off to one side, and the blood had run away from her body and collected near the grass.

The tent was airless, hot and silent except for the *click click* of the CSI's camera. There was a hint of Girl Guide expedition about the musty smell, but the prevalent odour was that of death. Rot set in soon after a human organism took its last breath, and the flies weren't very far behind, regardless of the season. Kelly knew the body hadn't lain there long because the fitness trainer had seen the victim run past, alive and well, around one o'clock.

She greeted the CSI. *Click click.*

'Two single knife wounds, consistent with a surprise attack. No defence wounds. No weapons, though forensics are searching. Both wounds are very deep and hit major arteries. It's very specific: femoral artery and aorta.'

'Skilled.'

It gave Kelly another scenario: gang initiation. It'd become more and more prevalent, and random victims were selected as well as rival gang members. Ella Watson didn't look to Kelly like a gang member, and she could see clearly now that this was no robbery because of the stunning ruby ring on her right hand and the diamond-laden wedding bands on her left. Her iPhone still sat in the running wallet and the woman wore an expensive watch.

Kelly had already got her team back at Eden House working initial background on the Watson family. They lived in a huge pad on Ullswater that was probably worth three million quid. Ella was a well-to-do middle-class housewife. A text came through with an attached copy of her driving licence and passport: Kelly could see immediately that the photos were of the woman in front of her.

She approached the body.

'The perp must have been covered in blood,' she said as she walked around the corpse, looking at it closely, studying its final position. There were no bloody foot-prints leading away and not much splatter at all. 'Or maybe not: it was quick, she hardly moved,' she added, thinking aloud. They all did it as a matter of course.

The CSI nodded. 'She's tried to use her hands to cover the wound, and collapsed. God, what a way to go.'

The body was surrounded by plastic number markers, next to items of interest. Kelly would have to give the go-ahead for them to be removed and bagged. Ella's headphones still lay where they'd presumably been knocked off by the impact of the attack.

'She might have stood a chance if she hadn't been wearing those.' The CSI pointed. Kelly shivered; she'd been on plenty of runs alone, wearing headphones, much to the annoyance of Johnny, who told her never to do so, no matter where she was.

She wouldn't do it again.

She looked at the victim's face. Her eyes were closed and she looked at peace, despite the carnage below. It looked as though she'd tried to get into the foetal position. The speed of the attack meant that the entry points of the blade were either expert or extremely lucky. Gang-style attacks usually aimed for just those areas, though the perps were rarely expert. Ted would be able to clarify it for her.

Knives. They were becoming endemic. Bravado made a lot of youngsters bold, and that was why so many of them died: they thought they could handle a knife fight. It was the biggest myth circulating around hormonally imbal-anced boys needing a release for their passions in between shagging. Like general elections, knife fights weren't won; they were lost. But this had been no fight.

She took a sketchpad out of her bag and began logging the scene in her own way. She didn't use computer-aided technology at this stage because she wanted to remember the scene as she saw it. As she worked, she confirmed with the photographer that she'd got certain shots and angles.

She was interrupted by a phone call from the coroner. She left the tent and breathed fresh air, tucking her sketchpad under her arm.

It was before they'd gone to Florida that she'd first called him Dad. It had been a slip of the tongue, and had been out before she could help it. She'd been about to apologise, but Ted had stopped her, saying he liked it. At work, though, in her professional capacity, she addressed him formally. He was on speaker phone and informed her that he was parking his car. She removed the plastic gloves and shoe covers and walked along the path to where she could see the police perimeter. When she spotted him, she waved and went to meet him. She wanted to hug him but held back. He winked, knowing her well.

'You've barely been back five minutes,' he said.

'Middle-aged woman, looks like a contract hit to me,' she said. 'No robbery: it was quick and clinical. It's a bit too clean for a gang initiation, and there haven't been any escalation indicators from known members round here. I checked.'

Ted accepted gloves and shoe covers and Kelly walked with him back to the tent. The professionals inside all knew the coroner, and the air shifted slightly. Somebody senior and important had just entered, and it made the situation graver. Ted Wallis was also physically impressive: his voice, his demeanour and his dress all indicated a man of wisdom and experience, and he automatically garnered respect. As he walked around the body, Kelly watched him, continuing to sketch and take notes. Ted spoke his thoughts and she didn't want to miss anything. She'd seen him at plenty of crime scenes before, and she enjoyed watching his approach.

He was a fit almost-sixty-year-old and showed no signs of slowing down. While they'd been in Florida, Johnny's daughter Josie had stayed with Ted, whom she considered like a grandfather to her. Apparently they'd been hiking together. They'd obviously had a blast and Josie had been spoiled, while Ted looked more than just healthy and happy; he looked revitalised and younger.

He knelt down to peer into Ella Watson's face. Then he moved behind her and examined the wounds with a magnifying glass. With his other hand, he pulled her tight running clothes away with a pair of long tweezers, turning his head this way and that.

'These punctures come from different directions, Kelly.'

She went to him and bent over.

'Look, this one looks as though the force came from here and upwards.' It was the cut in her groin that he referred to, which had sliced her femoral artery.

'This one came from above and from this side.' He pointed to the gash in her abdomen, which had severed her aorta. 'So unless your killer moved around her in some kind of dance, which is highly unlikely, given that there are no prints in the blood, I'd wager you have two.'

Chapter 3

Thomas Watson's mouth was dry. The drive from the golf club to his home on the shore of Ullswater was longer than he'd ever imagined. No one had told him what was going on. His gut sat in his toes all the way.

Why would the police have Ella's phone?

All they'd said to him was that they'd found it and they needed to speak to him urgently. They'd offered to send a car, but he'd refused. Jordan and Millie were at school until gone five p.m. He wanted to be at home. It made him feel closer to his wife, even though he had no idea what it was the police wanted with him.

He'd called the closest of her friends on his way back on hands-free. None of them had talked to her or seen her.

Maybe it was about the children. He called the school, who confirmed that Jordan and Millie were in their lessons and everything was normal.

Normal.

Why would the police, who were rushed off their feet, under-resourced and stretched to breaking, want to send a car for him to retrieve a lost phone?

His hands shook as he gripped the wheel, tighter and tighter. He willed himself to calm down, theories about what the police wanted whirring around his head. Surely if anything terrible had happened, Ella would have told him herself. Unless she couldn't. He told himself that the phone had been found after she had clumsily dropped it out of her always open bag – a habit he admonished her for – and it had been handed in. That was all. She'd been heading into town to do chores, and she'd mentioned a run. That was it: maybe she'd dropped her phone running and was wandering around looking for it. He often couldn't get through to her when she was running; it was as if she fell off the edge of the earth.

Don't worry…

She was probably at home, hoovering, or out in the garden, oblivious to the fact that she'd caused a fuss. Perhaps she was in the bath.

He drove on autopilot, having negotiated the tiny lanes thousands of times. But today, he didn't take any notice of the colour of the sky when it hit the lake, or the birds of prey circling over a field, or even the smiles on faces satisfied with their hike for the day and heading to pubs.

He kept experiencing waves of nausea and fought to concentrate. He was shocked when he arrived at the entrance to his driveway, because he recalled none of the journey. He pulled off the road and drove through the trees to where two police cars waited for him. Two, not one. As he got closer to the house, the doors of the cars opened and two plain-clothes officers climbed out of one, and two uniforms out of the other. He tried to read their faces, but they weren't looking at him.

His hands shook as he parked and got out. His chest felt as though it was on fire. One of the uniforms came towards him and introduced himself, asking if they could go inside. He was firm but gentle: the voice of pity.

Thomas had written enough reports and fired enough people to know that a shitstorm was coming. He swallowed hard and fiddled with something. He dropped his keys and bent to pick them up.

'What's all this about?' He couldn't bear to enquire after his wife by name.

'Can we go inside, sir?'

Thomas looked away from them and found the correct key, putting it in the door and turning it. The door swung opened and he stepped inside, wanting to run straight out the back, delaying the horror of the unknown.

The house felt stiflingly hot. He led them into the small room at the front. It was originally a study, though since Thomas had retired, it had become a storage room for paperwork and books, and a place where the children could complete homework in peace if they wanted to use the Mac. He fixed his eyes on the desk and saw Ella sitting there booking a holiday, just weeks ago. He spun around and saw that the two uniformed officers had followed him in.

'Goodness me, can you put me out of my misery now? I don't think you chaps would send the cavalry for a lost phone?' It was a rhetorical question but one that he secretly hoped would be answered with: don't worry, everything is fine. Ella's most hated word: fine. He swallowed hard.

'Sir, can you confirm that you are Thomas Watson, husband of Ella Watson?'

Thomas nodded. 'Yes,' he said quickly.

'We have some extremely bad news.' They were warning him, to take away the shock. He groped behind him for a chair to steady himself. His knees were weak and his bladder felt loose. Why did he need to pee?

'We believe that your wife was a victim of crime this afternoon and we need to inform you that she has died from her wounds, sir.'

Thomas's knees gave way and he slumped onto the chair behind him. He couldn't breathe properly. The officer went to him and knelt down. He'd already removed his hat outside, and Thomas noticed that he was young.

'Sir, do you understand what we've told you?'

Inside, he wanted to scream, but he simply nodded. 'Wait, no, how do you know? You said you believe, not that you know. Could there have been a mistake?'

'We checked with the DVLA and the Passport Office, sir. We're sure. This is Ella?'

Thomas was shown his wife's driving licence, which was registered to her Range Rover.

'The vehicle is parked at Potton Park in Penrith, sir, close to where the crime took place.'

Thomas looked up at the officer and felt his breathing slow and a loud humming enter his head. He was aware of nodding. The officer continued to talk, but it sounded like dull thuds in his head. He stared at him but couldn't work out what he was saying. One of the plain-clothes officers came into the room and introduced himself. He was tall and broad and accompanied by a tiny female, who also looked terribly young. The police force was staffed by babies now, Thomas thought.

'I'm Detective Constable Rob Shawcross and this is Detective Constable Emma Hide. You've had a huge shock, Mr Watson, and it doesn't seem fair at the moment, but we'd like to ask you some questions.'

Reality flooded Thomas's skull and he began to understand what was happening once more.

'Me? Why?' He turned from one to the other, feeling like a vulnerable child being scolded by the headmaster. He couldn't be living through this, but he was.

'Mrs Watson was attacked, sir. It's a murder inquiry.'

Waves of nausea hit him anew.

'Where is she?' He couldn't hear himself, was unaware of his mouth muscles working, so wasn't sure if he made sense.

'She's being taken to the Penrith and Lakes Hospital. We would like you to confirm her identify formally, but there's no rush at the moment.'

'I want to see her!' He stood up, but felt faint and sat back down again. 'The children!' He looked at his watch, but tears blurred his vision. He heard his voice but didn't own it. It was just a noise that emanated from his throat; it wasn't his. He had no control over it. His legs felt wobbly, even though he was sitting down, and he felt hot. Then cold.

'I'm sorry.' It was the young officer called Emma who spoke.

'There must be some mistake. I... I can't...'

It was too much. Thomas's body began to shut down and his vision grew fuzzy. He was aware of somebody leaving the room and coming back with water. Minutes seemed like hours and the room felt as though it would suffocate him.

'I have to get out of here. My children...'

'We've arranged for them to be brought home. Is there somebody you'd like to be here with you?' It was the tall man who spoke.

Thomas put his head in his hands.

'Let me introduce you to a very experienced liaison officer. This is…'

He heard words and nodded, but he felt other-worldly. He paid attention when he heard the tall man mention the investigation, and it dawned on him that they'd have to rule him out. He'd seen it in the press and knew that wives were usually battered and dispatched by spouses. It was a fact. Fresh horror assaulted him.

'Mr Watson. I know it's the most distressing time and you're in shock. But to find out who did this, we need you to focus and try to answer some of our questions. It will help our inquiry if we can start with these questions straight away. I'm sorry, I know it seems harsh, but it will help us to catch who did this to Ella. If you can't manage it right now, though, that's all right.'

Thomas stared. 'What happened?'

'She was stabbed. It appears that she was jogging. Did you know that she was going running in Potton Park?'

'No. I mean, yes. I knew she was running, but not where.' His voice dropped to a whisper. 'Stabbed.' He saw his children's faces and hung his head. Agony spread through his body and clarity began to shift the fug in his brain. His wife was dead.

'Thomas, was Ella in trouble with anyone? Had anyone threatened her?'

He was being interviewed. Two minutes after finding out that Ella had been stabbed to death, they were fucking interrogating him. He let out a sob and the tears came. The officers waited. They must do this all the time: tell relatives that their lives were broken, over, no more. His thoughts turned to Neil Ormond from the golf club: he was high up in the force, maybe he could help. It gave him something to help drag him out of the abominable hole he was sinking into.

'No, she wasn't in trouble. She never gave anyone any reason to hate her. How do I tell the children?'

'We can help you, Mr Watson.'

'Have you caught who did it?'

'Not yet. The perpetrator – or perpetrators – had fled the scene by the time the alarm was raised.'

'There was more than one? Oh God.'

'Nothing is confirmed yet, sir.'

He could tell they were working him out, and it dawned on him that, as prime suspect, they were trying to ascertain if he'd ordered a contract on his wife. He began to shake his head and sank his face into his hands.

'Had she argued with anyone recently?'

'No.'

'Was she in debt?'

'No.'

'Was your marriage a happy one?'

He looked up into the eyes of the female detective and held them. She was rather beautiful and he felt sorry for her having to ask such impertinent questions.

'Yes. Very.'

They said a few more things about searches and forensics, but he'd closed down. As they left, he remained in the same position.

–

Outside, Rob and Emma exchanged a few early thoughts. In a minute, they'd head back to Eden House, leaving the liaison team to do what it did best. They didn't want to hang around to see the kids. It was unprofessional and would be too overwhelming for them. They'd got what they wanted: an initial assessment of Thomas Watson, as well as the family home. They'd call Kelly from the car.

Chapter 4

Jackson Akers returned to his flat on the Beacon Estate in Penrith. He'd been at a friend's all night and he needed to sleep off the party. His normal routine consisted of fixing bikes during the day, for a modest income, and running errands at night, a more lucrative but risky trade. Sometimes the two overlapped. He gave little thought to either occupation, apart from the fact that he preferred fixing bikes. He'd been told at school, a long time ago, that he had a flair for taking stuff apart and putting it back together. He reckoned he got it from being locked in his room with radios, CD players, TVs and other hot kit, nicked by his dad and stored at their two-bedroom apartment in Wordsworth Towers. The same block of flats where he lived now.

At least he'd thought the bloke was his dad, until he never came home one day and his mum told him the truth. He was seven when he found out that his real father was in prison, with no possibility of parole until 2031. The man he'd thought was his dad, the man who'd locked him in the room with the stolen goods, beaten him, spat at him and generally treated him like shit, was some arsehole she'd shacked up with because she was lonely and he brought in cash.

He never saw that bitch no more.

They said at school that he was wilfully disruptive. They said he never showed a desire to learn. They said he was angry and violent. And they said he'd never amount to anything.

The thing was, though, that Jackson found it hard to see what school was all about. It seemed to him like you just got herded into a classroom, told stupid shit about stuff that didn't matter, ordered to do shit that got you nowhere, and given a piece of paper saying you could add up or write an essay at the end of it. He never saw any essay about fixing bikes, nor any mathematical equation for staying alive on the streets at 3 a.m. School bore no resemblance whatsoever to the values and skills he needed to survive. And until it did, boys like him would keep turning down a different road and travelling their own way.

One of his favourite artists played from a Bluetooth speaker. It was drill and rap music: something else you didn't learn in school. The language of kids on the street was unrepresented by the mainstream, and they had to express themselves any way they knew. The words – mainly banned on conventional digital outlets – were different to those used by 'normal' people, but that was the point. Those on the fringes of society, put there by those running that society, needed their own language to stay safe.

He'd begun writing his own raps when he was fourteen years old. He never told anyone. Only recently, after a gig where he met the artist, had he been encouraged to send his work to studios. He didn't receive many replies, but those he did advised him not to give up, and let him down gently by saying the time wasn't right. The singer he'd met at that gig inspired him to keep going and he sent more and more work to agents and talent scouts every month. He worked on a rap in his head now, drumming his feet into the kitchen lino and tapping on his leg as his stomach rumbled.

He was hungry and looked in his fridge. There was half a tin of beans and some slices of bread. He toasted the bread, threw a wedge of Cheddar on top, heated it under the grill, topped it with the beans and slathered brown sauce over the whole lot. As he sat down to eat, he looked at his watch. He had a package to collect soon. He never asked what was inside them, but he didn't need to; he had a pretty good idea. Everyone knew that if the plods came asking, no one knew nothing.

Say nuffin'…

The worst thing anybody could ever do was be a grass. Snitches died. Everyone knew that. They bled out in dark alleyways, with a home-made knife sticking out of their femoral artery. It was the quickest way to kill and if you were associated with a gang, you knew it. Man, it was going crazy at the minute, with sometimes fifteen stabbings reported up and down the country every weekend, from Manchester to London. There'd even been shootings. The newspapers were creaming themselves over the headlines, the stories making it to the front page every day, overshadowing even Brexit negotiations.

Fucking Brexit: who cared, man?

What the newspapers didn't report was that knife crime was just as bad out of London as it was in it. And by concentrating on the capital, they gave breathing space to those intent on controlling their gang members in the provinces. In Penrith, they had visitors from Manchester,

Liverpool, Glasgow and Aberdeen all the time. A gang was a transient being, like a locomotive: it picked up at every stop. As long as everyone knew the rules, they all co-existed side by side. It was a loose term for a way of life that gave allegiance to those who were hard and mean enough to take control. As such, it was precarious at best. There were no membership contracts or fees; the ultimate price was your life. For the past couple of years, the Cotton brothers had managed the estates in and around Penrith, from where they ran county-lines drug operations and kept rivals in check. The most important thing on the streets was to avoid aggro with the brothers, who thought nothing of ordering a hit or doing it themselves. They were both mean motherfuckers.

Jackson stayed independent by the skin of his teeth. He was in charge of his own yard, and he came and went when he pleased; he earned his own money and he never messed with girls who were owned by gang members. There was one sure way of getting sliced, and that was fucking a gang girl. He played the game and knew how to work all sides expertly. He was a gold mine of information and made it his business to gather it, in all its forms, for insurance. Crucially, he gave no one a reason to come after him. He did his work and kept his mouth shut, and everyone was happy. So far. He kept out of trouble by making himself necessary. Twenty years old was senior in terms of the street, and he knew a lot of shit.

Sure, he saw people hunted down and taken out, but that was their deal, not his. He'd survived this far, and had no intention of changing anything. Not one thing. Say nuffin'.

Man, he was tired. He'd been up all night watching dirty girls rub themselves up and down on boys' knees, *doin' their ting*, trying to impress and score. The music had been dope, though. And there'd been no blue lights disturbing the peace, though that was no surprise. On the Beacon Estate, nobody dared call the rozzers on one of their own. For years now, the police had avoided the hottest spots on the estate, and word had it that it was because somebody had done a deal with the law. Jackson said nothing. He'd seen them coming down and stopping and searching anyone looking like they were members – pretty much any male with a hoody – searching for drugs and weapons, but the visits had stopped a few years back and Jackson knew why. The pigs had a network of informers who traded in information. Maybe even the Cotton brothers were involved.

Say nuffin'.

Fresh drill music from London had flooded two flats for most of the night, and his head hurt like it always did after such events. He felt sorry for the other residents, especially the older ones, but that was the way of it and no one interfered. At the moment, he had good rap with the Cotton brothers. For the time being, they were in charge and Jackson intended to do everything in his power to stay onside. All street power was temporary – another thing they never taught in school – and it was only a matter of time before somebody else stepped up to the plate and the Cotton brothers were taken care of.

Members existed in the shadows of the estate, lurking in garages, flats and underground parking lots, their business mainly executed at night. During the day, the estate was fairly quiet and residents breathed a sigh of relief, going about their lives free of harassment. Jackson had once seen the Cotton brothers abusing an old guy, teasing him by taking his shopping away and tearing up his paper. Eventually the man had given them twenty quid and they'd shaken hands. The image stuck. It seemed heartless, but at least the guy had lived. It was nothing new: stamping your authority on a yard. The Cotton brothers were from Lancaster and had to get to know the locals properly. If anyone disagreed, they ended up in hospital.

With the coppers rarely coming to the estate now, the area was essentially independent from the law. The gang leaders were the law, and justice was served as they saw fit. Even if a crime was reported to the cops – which rarely happened – they'd find no evidence. It was in the constabulary's best interest to leave the place alone. Attempts at interfering in estate matters would result in fucking up police achievement targets, so they stayed away. Patrol cars stuck to the edges and avoided the roads leading into the heart of the territory. There had been an investigation into a stabbing last month, but the victim had refused to press charges. Most events went unreported anyhow. Victims got patched up in bedrooms, away from the traceable computer hard drives in hospital. Some died. They weren't missed.

As soon as he'd received and offloaded the package, he'd crawl into bed and sleep straight for twelve hours. Tomorrow he had stuff to do.

Chapter 5

Kelly and Ted walked together across the park in the direction of the Beacon Estate. She took the call from Rob and nodded. Then she hung up and turned to Ted.

'The husband is suitably devastated.'

'They always are.'

'Not always. Remember Chris Watts? Colorado? Killed his pregnant wife and two young daughters?'

'Ah yes, fiddled with his mobile phone and got more animated about the TV remote than the disappearance of his family.'

'Yep. Sometimes they act too much.'

'So, in this case?'

'I sent two officers who are top notch. They read character excellently. Their hunch is that he's genuine. I'll know more when we bring him in.'

They walked on, taking their time to look around them.

'If it was me, I'd come this way rather than risk getting caught at the park entrance. They would have been able to hear the fitness trainer shouting too, so would have needed to go in the opposite direction.'

Ted agreed.

The sky was becoming dark; it was almost four o'clock. DC Hide had also informed Kelly that Thomas Watson had agreed to identify Ella's body once he'd seen his children. It was a laborious and often frustrating process. The body had to be moved to the mortuary – signed off by Ted – then the next-of-kin had to be transported there and accompanied, and given time to say goodbye. It didn't always go to plan. Kelly's gut told her to be there when Thomas Watson went to the hospital. Until that time, Ella would be placed in cold storage. Before her husband went in, he'd also have to be informed that he wouldn't be allowed to touch her until after the autopsy. This was always the single worst thing – and there were plenty – about a murder inquiry of a loved one.

'It's a grim business, Kelly,' Ted said. 'Stick to the facts; they always lead you to the right place eventually. This is a sorry-looking place.'

They'd arrived at a gate that opened onto a road at the back of the estate. There were garages and a pavement and that was it: no trees, plants, cars or people, giving it the air of an abandoned other-world. Perfect to hide in.

'Can you see any cameras?'

'Nope. I didn't expect to, but it's still disappointing. I think we need to do door-to-door starting with those flats. There's no line of sight to where Ella actually died, but from the upper floors, the park will be clearly visible.'

'I'll walk you back to your car,' Ted said.

They turned around and made their way back. They said goodbye and made plans to meet up soon, as father and daughter rather than investigators of slaughter.

It was going to be a long evening. In her head, Kelly set about putting together an investigating team of officers. Before she allocated jobs, she'd need to introduce them to the crime scene. It was fresh in her mind and she'd already begun to prioritise.

When she returned to Eden House, she went straight to the coffee machine and then sat at her desk collating what they had so far, including the disturbing collection of forensic photographs. Death was the most personal and private rite of passage, unless you were murdered, when it became a public display of a person's life; like some grim documentary. After a few days, they'd all be immune to the blood and gore as they filed past the grisly collage posted carefully on the incident board.

It was six o'clock before she briefed her squad. They had little to go on, but the first day or two was always the calm before the storm. Thomas Watson had provided the names of Ella's friends and associates as well as a recent photograph to be circulated on the evening news. A fatal stabbing in broad daylight, in a park used by families, should garner a positive response. It was the type of case that tended to horrify local residents, and Kelly expected a flood of phone calls and emails. It was also shocking enough to catch the attention of the national media. It was everyone's worst nightmare: a random stabbing of somebody in the wrong place at the wrong time. If that was indeed the case.

The incident rooms at Eden House were all on the top floor, which was where Kelly's office was too. Ranks higher than detective inspector were housed in their ivory tower at HQ, on the outskirts of Penrith, in a grand old gaff hidden behind bushes away from prying eyes. It was the headquarters for the whole Cumbrian constabulary, but Kelly had no desire to work there. Promotion, should it ever come, would have to be elsewhere for her.

She'd begun to create an incident map for the case, with the photo of Ella at the centre. She always did it: seeing the victim's face every day had the effect of galvanising her team and reminding them what they were fighting for. She entered the incident room and perched on the edge of a desk. Her team waited.

'Guv, emergency news bulletin sorted for six thirty,' DS Kate Umshaw announced. DS Umshaw was the mother hen of the team, making sure everybody was happy and supplied with tea and cake. She was also hard as nails.

'Thanks, Kate,' Kelly said. The office was warm from the aged radiators, and they needed the lights on. It was beginning to feel like winter. The sky outside was black, and snow was predicted. 'Perimeter?' she asked.

DC Rob Shawcross answered. 'We've got uniforms at every entrance to the park, as well as on the main roads in and out of the area; they're stopping every car, bicycle and pedestrian and taking statements.' DC Shawcross was her Great Dane, keeping guard over his master, ready to pounce.

'Excellent. Any sign of the weapon? Or weapons? We won't know which until the coroner's done.'

'Not yet, guv. Ten officers did a shoulder-to-shoulder search for one hundred metres in all directions. They haven't got the manpower to go further yet.'

'Appeal for public help and get that coordinated, Will.'

He nodded. DS Will Phillips was her middle-distance champion, her plodder, who never failed to churn out answers and provide solid graft.

'What about the fitness trainer?'

'He said he saw her run past at around 1.15 p.m. His class finished at 1.20. It was as he was leaving that he saw her body.'

'Christ, so a five-minute window. Which direction was she running?'

'South, judging from where she parked her car, following the figure-of-eight path from the splash park towards the pond.'

'And he didn't hear her scream? The speed of the attack and the fact that she didn't even get her phone out of her running wallet suggests they came from behind, yet the trainer saw no one else? Get a map up,' Kelly said. 'Let's see where they could have come from. I think I have an idea, though.'

DC Shawcross tapped his keyboard, and a map of Potton Park and the surrounding area appeared on the white incident board, covering a four-mile radius. Kelly would be losing him to paternity leave shortly; his girl-friend Mia was due in early December but already ready to pop. It was appalling timing, but no one would feel worse about it than Rob. She'd have to make sure he stayed away should the case not be wrapped up by then, though he'd be sorely missed. He was their computer nerd and loved nothing more than creating logarithms and mapping aids to close down an investigation in its tracks. She had every faith in the rest of her team: young DC Emma Hide, who was all passion; DS Phillips, who lived and breathed protocol, and DS Umshaw, her battle-scarred workhorse.

Someone dimmed the lights, and Kelly picked up a long ruler and approached the board; her body became part of the map and she looked like a swamp dweller, covered in foliage and scarred earth.

'The training session was here.' She pointed to the glade in which the trainer had been giving a class to fourteen women. Their names and contact details had all been supplied and Kelly had uniforms tracking them down for statements. 'Ella Watson was running this way.' She indicated where Ella had collapsed and the direction from which she'd come. 'If the trainer didn't see anyone else, then the killers had to have come from the bushes here, or from this direction.' She followed the ruler beyond the park. It was a direct line to the outskirts of the Beacon Estate.

'I walked this route, past the pond, with the coroner this afternoon. It's the most convincing theory. This area here is totally deserted and isolated. It's just a few garages, but these flats here are the nearest residences.'

'Boss, you said killers, plural? Is that now confirmed?' DC Hide asked.

'Not a hundred per cent. As you know, the coroner detected that the stab wounds were inflicted from two different directions. In his opinion – and I agree – it's highly unusual for one perp to change position, especially during such a flash attack. He'll confirm after the autopsy.' Kelly paused. 'What's life on the Beacon Estate like these days?'

She watched as people shifted in their seats.

'That bad? Will? You've got buddies in patrol units – you know, the ones you left behind to lord it about up here with us?' It got a laugh and Will took it well. It was true, he had close ties to bobbies on the beat.

'It's not good, boss. It's like shovelling shit while the horse is still having a dump, if you don't mind the expression.'

'Not at all, I rather like it,' Kelly said. 'Any more than usual? What are the stats that we don't know about?' She was referring to crime that didn't get picked up by an investigative team – such as complaints and disturbances not likely to be charged – or non-serious crime dealt with by uniforms. Non-serious crime could mean anything from burglary to buggery, all depending on if it was reported, and by whom.

'Very little goes beyond the initial responder. There are plenty of burglaries, domestics, sexual assaults, actual assaults and general shit like drug abuse and kids pissing around, but that's as far as it goes; no one wants to press charges or give evidence. It's frustrating. It makes it difficult to gain a clear picture at all.'

'And demoralising, I expect?' Kelly asked.

'Exactly,' Will agreed.

'Has lethargy set in? Do squad cars even go there much?' It was a serious question.

Will didn't answer. It said everything.

'So who's in charge?' she asked.

Will looked uncomfortable. Kelly waited.

'There's a few main players who are what you might term untouchable,' he said eventually.

'Untouchable? Jesus. Is it the Wild West?' Kelly got up and went to a swivel chair, sitting down hard in it and spinning around, looking at the map. She was hungry and tired. Her holiday had lulled her into a false sense of life being easy. It wasn't that long until Christmas, and a year since her mother had died.

'Foot patrols?' she asked.

'Cutbacks. The odd patrol drives through. I believe there is a network of informants.'

Kelly made a note to ask around at HQ about registered confidential informants relating to the Beacon Estate. Snouts and narks were usually paid handsomely, but they were becoming rarer, due to the dangers associated with being a rat. The whole system had also become heavily regulated, rendering it somewhat ineffectual since the days of *The Sweeney*. But if Will said it went on, then she trusted him.

'Has anyone else anything to add?' she asked.

No one answered.

'Right, let's be clear. Here's my crime-scene assessment.' She stood up and went to her laptop. The lights went back on. She'd mentally prepared for what she wanted out of her team, and this was where the investigation began. She brought up the CSA, the document that every detective in charge of a crime scene had to process. It was seventy pages long. She wasn't about to bore them with vehicle interiors, entomology or the absence of fire damage, which everyone knew to be irrelevant for Ella; however, there were some pertinent points to be noted.

The first involved her rough sketch of the scene. In essence it was just a pencil drawing, but Kelly liked to make hers as detailed as possible; it might have to stand up in court one day. She'd drawn Ella Watson's body where it fell, on the road through the park, and added the treeline, the training class and the pond and splash pool. Now she electronically added the direction Ella was running in, and the Beacon Estate.

'We need to search this pond. No evidence of sexual assault; the timeline indicates there wouldn't have been time, and her clothes didn't appear tampered with. So motive seems to be pure and simple: murder. Estimated time of death, agreed on scene by the coroner and given by the witness testimony of the trainer, is 1.15 to 1.20 p.m. Blood flow was consistent with bleeding out, spatter consistent with high-velocity pressure spurting.' She turned to her team. 'So what does this mean?'

'Surprise attack. Quick, passionless, violent and opportunistic.' It was Emma Hide who spoke first.

'I agree. Motive for murder?'

'Someone ordered them to do it,' Emma replied.

'Precisely. Whoever did this didn't do it for themselves, they did it for someone else. I'm talking to the husband as soon as he's identified the body. Liaison officers will stay with the family as long as necessary. Mr Watson's mother is on her way from Manchester to stay with them. We start there. Now, on to the photography and evidence lists. Very little, I'm afraid. Again, the speed of the attack makes our job that much harder. The coroner said they might have got away without any blood on them too, amazingly. Her wounds spurted in front of her and away to the side of the road. They were very likely behind her: this would explain the headphones being knocked off.'

She brought up the crime-scene photo of Ella lying on her side, her headphones a foot away in a pool of undisturbed blood. It was a singularly tragic scene. Ella Watson was about the same age as DS Umshaw, who also had teenage children.

'You can see from the photo that she's still wearing her watch and expensive rings, and her iPhone X is still in the running wallet. No robbery.' Nobody spoke. 'Mr Watson has been informed that they'll have to vacate the family home while we undertake a thorough forensic search. If I can, I'll organise it for first thing tomorrow. The warrant has already been requested. Kate, I want you to coordinate the land searches and door-to-door witness statements. Will, you and I will continue to dig around into violent crime and policing on the Beacon Estate. Rob, can you work on an interactive map of the estate and Potton Park. And Emma, can you coordinate the physical evidence and liaise with the labs; also collate all the information from the two house searches this morning – they should have both been completed. I think that's all for now.'

Her team dissipated and Kelly went to her office and logged on to her computer to finish the report. A police underwater search team from Lancaster had replied to her email and said they could schedule a search of the pond first thing tomorrow. She replied telling them the rendezvous point. They could be there at 10 a.m.

She also had an email from Superintendent Neil Ormond at HQ. A quick glance at it left her speechless. Neil Ormond had been on the force for the whole of Kelly's life. He was a giant man with keen eyes who sucked up the air in a room. He wasn't known for his by-the-book approach but more for his opinionated damnation of do-gooders. She reread the email and stared at the screen.

Neil Ormond and Thomas Watson were golfing buddies.

Several problems swirled around her head. One was the huge conflict of interest. A plus side was that it might mean sudden miraculous funding for policing the Beacon Estate.

But what really bothered her was the super's language. He referred to Ella Watson as a 'respectable, law-abiding woman' and Kelly couldn't help thinking that if the victim had been a lowlife from the estate, he would have considered that she'd deserved her fate. It reminded her of the Yorkshire Ripper case, when the victims weren't taken so seriously due to their immoral activities as supposed prostitutes. Peter Sutcliffe got away with his crimes for years longer than he should have.

HOLMES, the pithy and conveniently memorable acronym for the Home Office Large Major Enquiry System, came into use as a direct result of that case, which had generated so many leads that it was estimated it would have taken decades to plough through them had Sutcliffe not been finally picked up on a minor traffic offence and confessed. It was a period in the force that had changed everything. The fact that Kelly was standing here today, leading a serious crime unit rather than making the tea, was down to that case.

Ormond told her that he was going to come down hard on those responsible for Ella Watson's murder, but Kelly didn't think for a second that he should be anywhere near the investigation. He made it clear that he wanted the case to be high profile. Honourable middle-class white lady gets whacked, and HQ want an abrupt end to knife crime. It would look good on all sides. The whole tone of the email sat uncomfortably with her, and she decided to confront him face to face.

Chapter 6

Kelly drove to the constabulary headquarters on the perimeter of Penrith. If Superintendent Ormond was putting his head above the parapet and admitting this was a personal matter, then for one, he shouldn't have direct executive power over the case; and two, he could give her an interview about his friends the Watsons.

She'd been many times before to the dated stone and glass building languishing peacefully behind trees, away from the harsh day-to-day working of case files. She appreciated that this was where the brains were. The top brass, who'd spent their lives on the force, shaping policy, doing their best, diving for cover from the yo-yo dizziness of consecutive governments barking their U-turns. It wasn't for her. She had an inkling that the Ella Watson case was about to turn into a circus, and she needed advice.

She parked her car and signed in at the reception desk. She was given a new pass to wear as well as her Eden House one and shown through a labyrinth of offices. Finally she was left at a door and informed that she was to knock and go in: Superintendent Ormond was expecting her. She did so, and his voice boomed from within.

Neil Ormond was an old-fashioned copper: as big as a house, steely-eyed, and welcoming as a teddy bear. He beamed at her, but also looked at his watch: it was gone 7 p.m.

'DI Porter, you've been making quite a name for yourself.'

'In a good way, I hope, sir.'

'Indeed, very.'

'Thank you, sir. Just doing my job.'

'Of course you are, and damn fine at it you are. Well done. Promotion on the cards, I'm sure.'

'I'd rather stay operational, sir.'

'I bet you would. Bloody good at it. You've got the nose, Porter. What can I do for you? Is this about Ella Watson?'

'Yes, sir.'

'Sit down. Coffee?'

'Yes, thank you, sir.'

He buzzed a junior, no doubt sitting close by to keep his cup topped up all day. She'd bet her life it was a woman: some habits never fully died out. Sure enough, a woman in uniform scuttled in with a tray and placed it between them on the desk. Ormond didn't acknowledge it, and she left.

'Sir, I appreciated the candour in your email, and I'd like to go over a few things if I may?'

'Fire away. I want this bastard caught.'

'Possibly bastards plural, sir.'

'What?'

'Coroner is convinced there were two attackers. I'll confirm after the autopsy.'

Ormond looked a little confused and Kelly waited for him to gather his thoughts again. She went straight on to the reason she'd come.

'I'd like to find out how well you know the Watson family, sir. It could help our inquiry. Thomas Watson is, understandably, with his children at the moment and we haven't had a chance yet to interview him fully.'

'I understand. I met Tom when he moved to the area three years ago. Decent chap, friendly, genuine, and a golfer. That's where we met. I met Ella and the children when we invited them to ours for lunch one weekend. Lovely family, not a jot of badness between them. Kids doing well at school – they go to St Catherine's, I believe – and thoroughly hard-working, respectable people.'

That word again.

'It's appalling what's happened.'

'I know, sir. I'm sorry about your personal involvement. I presume, with respect, you'll be passing on this one? I'll keep it in-house and report to DCI Cane as always.'

'Not at all, I want to be informed every step of the way. You report direct to me, do you understand?'

Kelly's stomach felt heavy. 'Yes, sir.' Her hands were tied. She wasn't about to disagree with a superintendent and go behind his back. She'd have to put up with him breathing down her neck from now on until she cracked the case. However, the unorthodox nature of what he'd just asked her to do unsettled her. He was breaking protocol. No one was supposed to go unilateral on a case this huge, and there was a massive conflict of interest here. It was impossible for Ormond to be impartial.

'So, we're going with the gang lead, then? Residents of the Beacon Estate – high on drugs probably – attack an innocent woman who appears wealthy and get away with… what? A phone? A ten-pound note?'

Again, Kelly was perplexed by his frankly unprofessional approach to this case; he'd been off the street for too long.

'Sir, there are many theories and I doubt a gang hit is the one. It wasn't a robbery. Nothing was taken from Ella's body, and she was wearing expensive jewellery and had a top-of-the-range iPhone.'

Ormond looked shocked – no, irritated. He'd had it all sorted in his head, thought Kelly, which was exactly why she didn't want him on this case: he was making assumptions before the evidence was even in; it was the worst kind of police work. She had a horrible feeling that this could be the trickiest case she'd faced so far since moving back to Cumbria from the Met.

'We also haven't discounted the husband yet, sir. That's always the first port of call on the death of a spouse.'

'But that's ridiculous! Tom wouldn't…' He realised his mistake and trailed off. 'Of course, you're right. You have to carry out a full inquiry to rule him out. Let me know when you do, will you?'

'Yes, sir. Would you like me to keep you in the loop by email?'

'No, call me. Day or night. This is my mobile number.' He scribbled on a piece of paper and gave it to her. Her heart sank further. She finished her coffee.

'Did Ella Watson strike you as a happy person, sir?'

Ormond thought about his answer. He appeared guarded.

'I don't know what you mean, Porter. Happy how?'

'Did she come across as the woman who had it all, like I'm being told?'

'Now you mention it, she wasn't as relaxed as you would expect. There always seemed to be something on her mind, other than what was going on in the here and now, if you know what I mean.'

'I think I do. Did Tom ever share what she got up to during the day?'

'Men don't bother with that sort of niff-naff, Porter. I have no idea. She was a housewife, isn't that a job?'

'Of course, sir, but I'm trying to build up a picture of her character. Did she seem depressed?'

'Like I said, she sometimes came across as deep in thought. A bit serious, I suppose.'

'What about Tom, sir? What type of man is he?'

'Very accomplished. Enjoying his early retirement. His handicap is fifteen!' He looked away and coughed.

Kelly kept her face straight, deciding that Superintendent Ormond wasn't quite the legend she'd been led to believe.

'Sir, I wonder if you could assist me in gaining access to the criminal informant data regarding the Beacon Estate. One of my officers mentioned that policing there has declined sharply but that they do rely on informants.'

'It's your department, Porter, you should know.'

'Yes, sir, I understand that. However, I've only been in post for three years and have had very little to do with the Beacon Estate, perhaps for that very reason: because not much crime is investigated there after it's reported. Either charges are dropped or evidence is lacking. It's curious.'

'Oh, I don't know about that, I think it's normal for such a den of iniquity. Come on, Porter, you worked in London!'

She didn't know what to say. It was as if he was telling her that giving up on certain sections of society was normal, required even. It was not just old-fashioned, but dangerous.

'You could always speak to the patrols on the ground. They'll know any informers, I wager.'

'But aren't all informants supposed to be logged and regulated now, sir?'

His face went slightly pink. She'd come across as the girl from the city lording it over the sticks, and she could have kicked herself. She still had a lot to learn. He leaned across his desk and stared at her.

'Call me when this thing is done and dusted and I can announce it to the press. Definitely looks gang-related to me, though, Porter.'

She left the room and took a deep breath.

This wasn't going to be easy.

Chapter 7

Thomas Watson was a broken man.

After he'd spent some time with his children, he made the short journey with a liaison officer to the Penrith and Lakes Hospital, to identify the body of his wife. The woman who'd given birth to his kids, raised them to be the outstanding young people they were today; the woman who'd made him laugh and made him cry lay under a sheet on a cold metal table, lifeless and empty of breath.

He stumbled and almost fell, and the officer took his arm.

'You all right, sir? Would you like to sit down?' There were plastic chairs along the wall.

Thomas shook his head. It had been a hell of a day. The worst day of his life. Telling Jordan and Millie that they were never going to see their mother again. Ever.

They'd wanted to come to the hospital. He'd said no. Now he was regretting it. Selfishly, he wanted them here by his side, supporting him, because he didn't think he could go through with it on his own. He felt sick and leant against the wall.

'Would you like some water, sir?'

'No.' They carried on. A woman in a white coat waited for them, but he didn't look at her. He didn't want to see another sympathetic smile. He had no more tolerance for pity left inside him. His wife was dead. He was living a nightmare.

He was led into a room and he noticed that it was cold. The woman spoke gently and explained to him that in the next room was a glass screen, and beyond that a table on which lay the deceased, covered with a sheet. She would go behind the screen and lift the sheet, and he was to confirm or deny identity. For one crazy moment he realised that it might not be Ella in there: they could have made a tragic, ridiculous mistake. But then reality hit him like a steamroller and he rubbed his eyes. His heart pounded in his chest and his head felt odd. His vision blurred and his hands were sweaty and hot.

'Thomas?'

He looked at her. She was so young.

'It has been explained to you that you can't touch her?'

He nodded.

He'd been told that he couldn't hold his wife until after the autopsy. She was to be sliced up like some laboratory animal and he couldn't comfort her.

They went in. He swallowed hard and tried to keep the pain from exploding out of him. Another uniform was in the room, and Thomas realised that he was there as a heavy, to make sure he didn't go crazy and barge behind the screen to hold and kiss his dead wife. His stomach hit his knees as he turned and saw the table beyond the glass screen. The woman went behind the screen and looked at him. His hands were clammy and his throat constricted.

She turned back the sheet, just to Ella's neck. Thomas's legs collapsed and he fell to the floor, hitting it hard. He could hear himself babbling on about being sorry. A man's voice spoke and a hand helped him up.

'Thomas?'

'It's her. It's Ella.' The sobs came.

The sheet was replaced and the woman came back out of the room and indicated that it was time to leave. It was over. Thomas's whole body cried out to hold her, yearning for her to caress him, to take his hand and hug him in return. He could smell her perfume, bought last Christmas, still clinging to her dead skin. If only he could make love to her one last time and tell her how much he adored her. His face was soaking wet and snot dribbled down his chin.

The woman blocked his view and he turned towards the door. A cacophony of bangs and clangs bombarded his head. He couldn't remember getting the lift upstairs but found himself in an office. Somebody brought him coffee, and tissues.

A different woman sat opposite him – he'd lost count of everyone who'd dealt with him this afternoon – and he realised that now it was time for the questions. No doubt questions about his marriage. He knew the game: the police had to rule him out as a suspect. It was their job. He had to prove that he hadn't hired some thug to take Ella out. He looked at the woman intently. Her eyes were green and her hair was auburn. Her skin was clean and fresh like Ella's had been in life. The male uniformed officer who'd taken him downstairs stood behind her.

'Hello, Thomas – may I call you Thomas? I'm Detective Inspector Kelly Porter. Take your time.'

He took a sip of coffee and blew his nose. He must look like crap. He felt like crap. He took a deep breath.

'I'm ready,' he said. 'And you may call me Thomas.'

'Thank you. You understand that this is procedure.' He nodded. 'I'm very sorry for your loss. Mrs Watson – Ella – was a keen jogger, I believe?'

Was.

It crushed him. He nodded.

'Did she often run in Potton Park?'

He shook his head. 'The only reason she was there was because she was going shopping, doing errands, I don't know what. No, wait. Jordan said he'd broken his phone.'

'Your son, Jordan?'

Thomas nodded. 'Yes, she was going to the Apple Store.'

'Did you know that she was intending to run afterwards?'

'She did mention it, yes, but I had no idea where.'

'Did she know anybody in the area? Could she have arranged a meeting?'

'Potton Park? No. Her friends – our friends – all live outside town.'

'So she hadn't made arrangements to meet anyone in the park?'

'No, that's ridiculous, why would she do that?' He looked at the woman and realised that she was digging to see if Ella had been having an affair. He also realised that he had no idea if she had been. He couldn't prove or disprove the theory. DI Kelly Porter must have seen his confusion. She tried a different approach.

The direct one.

'Was she having an affair?'

'No.'

'To your knowledge?'

'To my knowledge. She was happy...' His voice wasn't convincing. She could easily have been having an affair. He searched his mind for evidence either way. They made love perhaps twice a month, sometimes more. It wasn't enough for him, but Ella's interest had waned. Had it waned because she was satisfied elsewhere? The DI read him well.

'Did she display any illicit behaviour?'

'How would I know? No, I don't think so. I never suspected that she was sneaking about, or making quiet phone calls, or hiding her phone: that's the sort of thing you mean?'

'Exactly.'

'No, then.'

'Thank you. To your knowledge, are you aware of anyone who might have wanted to hurt your wife?'

Past tense again. It stung.

'No.'

'Was she in debt, or in any kind of trouble financially?'

'No. Definitely not. I run the house finances. We're good.'

'I'm sorry, Mr Watson, but we'll need access to your financial records and her phone data, as well as any PCs she used in the house.'

'Of course. Do everything you need to do. You're going through the house tomorrow? I'm taking my mother and the children to a hotel nearby.'

'Which hotel?'

'The Peaks Bay.'

The DI scribbled a note. 'Did Ella display any unusual behaviour in the days and weeks leading up to her death?'

'Not that I can think of. I've tried to recall, but I can't think of anything.'

'Would you be willing to give a press statement?'

'An appeal?'

She nodded. He thought about it. It was perhaps one of the few things he could actually do to contribute to the investigation.

'Of course.'

'Would you consider allowing your children to join you?'

That one came from left field and smacked him in the kidneys. He felt the colour drain from his face. He had to hand it to the detective: she was ballsy. He understood the impact it could have: two teenagers begging the public for information about how their mum was butchered in broad daylight in a park.

It might make up for his ban on them coming to the hospital.

'I would. They're old enough to decide. I think, knowing the two of them, they'll say yes.'

'It will help. Someone out there knows who did this, and I'm going to find them.'

He looked at her again, and saw something in her eyes that he hadn't seen in a long time. Not since before he retired. It was a look very few people had: pure grit and determination. For the first time that day, he felt something akin to relief.

The detective held out her hand. He shook it. She had a strong grip. She smiled warmly at him.

'Take my card and call me — day or night — if anything comes to you. I mean absolutely anything; it could be the tiniest detail.'

'I will.' He took the card. 'Thank you, Detective.'

'Call me Kelly. How are the kids?'

'Awful. I just don't know what the future holds. I can't think. Ella was everything to us. She was everything to them. She does everything for them. Did. I can't even begin to think about filling that gaping hole.' The tears came again.

'Don't pull yourself to pieces. Allow yourself to be angry, or anything you want to be. It's early days.' She passed him another tissue and he held it to his eyes. 'Take it slowly; rely on friends and your mother. Take full advantage of the family liaison officers, they're excellent.'

He nodded.

'Have you heard of Neil Ormond?' he asked.

'Yes, I have.' Kelly concluded from the question that the super hadn't yet contacted his friend. Odd.

'Does he work here? He's a personal friend. I wondered if he could help us.'

'Superintendent Ormond is overseeing the case, Thomas. I report to him.'

Thomas's eyes widened. He tapped the table resolutely. 'Well, we're in safe hands then. Can I go now? I want to be with my children.'

'Of course.'

Chapter 8

Millie Watson buried her head in her pillow. Her bedroom was her place of safety and security. But it felt different now. She kept looking to the door, expecting Mum to come in and nag her about homework, or tell her that tea was ready, or ask if she'd fed the cat.

The pain was physical.

So was the anger. Dad knew they weren't stupid, and that they'd read about it online sooner or later. Mum had been stabbed to death. Stabbed. It made her feel sick.

Her pillow was sodden. She heard her phone ringing but ignored it. There was no point in anything. Food, drink, music, Instagram, and Snapchat: nothing interested her. Rupert, their ginger feline, snuggled up to her, and only the softness of his fur gave her any sense of reality. Every time she ran her hand over his ears and he purred gently, she felt something to hold onto, something to make sense of. She didn't trust anything else, not even being with her dad or Jordan. Dad was trying to keep his shit together, she knew that much. She'd screamed at him to lose it, to shout and punch something, but he refused. She knew he was doing it for their benefit, but it was driving her mad. Jordan was in his own room, hiding too. Grandma was with Dad and another man downstairs. They spoke in hushed whispers and Millie couldn't bear it.

She overheard the man telling her dad that his department was being given everything they needed. She heard
Dad call him Neil. She heard Neil call her mum's killer
a bastard. That was too good for whoever had done it.
They'd debated the death penalty at school and Millie
had listened to both sides, taking on board the whole
issue of human rights and forgiveness. But she wanted her
mother's killer to hang. No, in fact, she wanted to stab
him herself. There wasn't an ounce of doubt in her mind
that she could go through with it. Easy.

She heard Grandma crying, and she wanted to go to
her but didn't have the energy to move. Grandma had
hugged her and said things that Millie couldn't recall now;
she'd also made food that she couldn't remember eating.
She assumed it was shock that had made her zone out. No
one could say anything to make it better.

There was a light knock on her door and she ignored
it. If anyone came in, she'd roll over and pretend to
be asleep. Everyone thought she was traumatised. But
it wasn't trauma; it was fucking anger. Her mum was
the kindest, funniest, purest friend she had. She was her
soulmate and always had been. Not three seconds elapsed
before something popped into her head to tell her, and
now she couldn't. The realisation that she'd never see her
again hurt in every bone. Her heart felt as though it might
break, the pain was so bad, and she struggled to breathe,
willing herself to find a path through the fog. There was
another knock. She ignored it again, hoping that whoever
it was would just give up. The door opened and she closed
her eyes tightly, lying very still. They'd leave any moment,
she thought.

'Mills.' It was Jordan. 'I know you're not asleep, you muppet.'

'Fuck off.' It was an affectionate brush-off and she turned over and smiled weakly.

'How you doing?' he asked.

'Stupid question. Muppet,' she said.

He nodded, coming to the bed. She felt a kind of calm descend over her and realised that she wanted him in there. He wasn't behaving like Dad by pretending to be strong; he just was strong. He sat on the bed and stroked the cat. His eyes were as red as her own. She moved over and made room for him to lie down. Rupert accommodated him too. Jordan settled in a comfy position and they lay face to face, the cat between them.

'I overheard Dad talking to a policeman who came to the house in plain clothes. He's like the big cheese, a superintendent, and he plays golf with Dad. He said they're questioning people on the Beacon Estate. It sounds to me like they reckon it was an initiation thing, gang-related.' Jordan sniffed and wiped his hand over his face. Millie could tell that, like her, inside he was screaming to get his hands on the fucker who'd killed their mum.

Jordan was a quiet guy. He had girlfriends, he went to the gym, he partied, like all boys his age, but he also carried himself with dignity. Mum said so. Millie's friends all fancied him and she took the piss out of him about it. Sure, they fought, like all siblings, and they scrapped and chased each other around the house. But here, right now, on this bed, she felt like he was her world. She felt placid and safe with him and she hadn't thought to reach out. He'd done it and she was thankful. She stopped stroking the cat and propped herself up on her elbow.

'Initiation? What the actual fuck?' she said. Jordan's eyes burned with hate and Millie felt pride in him like she never had before. They could both stab the guy who'd done this, one hundred, two hundred, three hundred times, in the face, in the stomach, in the dick that he obviously thought was so big. She tasted acid in her mouth and Jordan reached out his hand to hers.

'I know what you're thinking,' he said. 'Stop it; it will tear you apart. I feel exactly the same. That bloke will catch them, you know, and when he does, I'll find a way to get to them. I promise.'

'Them?'

'Yeah, the police guy said they reckon there were two of them.'

'Oh my God, no!' She buried her face in Jordan's chest. The cat moved. Millie's shoulders shook and the sobs returned. Jordan held her as she cried, her whole body spasming with fresh waves of agony. She felt as though it would never end. Visions of her mother, surrounded by two strangers, knowing she was powerless to fight back, lying bleeding on the road on her own, with no one to help…

It was too much. If only she could wake up and start the day all over again. She'd never leave her mother, never allow her to go running alone; she'd force her to stay home…

Jordan never loosened his grip and she sank deeper into him, feeling his body, hot and tense, next to her. The image of battering whoever was responsible for murdering their beautiful mother burned in her head. She closed her eyes and howled.

Chapter 9

Kelly opened the front door of her small cottage in Pooley Bridge. Johnny had said he'd cook tonight. Josie, his daughter, was at her boyfriend's house. She spent more and more time with him. Callum was a thoroughly genuine young man, and both Kelly and Johnny liked him.

Her body was weary. It was gone 9 p.m. and there was nothing more she could do at the office. The night shift, patrolling the streets of Penrith, around Potton Park and the surrounding estates, were under strict instructions to call her should anything change, or a significant witness statement come in. It had been a harrowing day.

She dropped her bags and coat onto a chair in the hallway and stretched. She needed a shower. Johnny came from the lounge and opened his arms. He knew what she'd faced today. They'd spent three whole weeks sailing around the Florida Keys and it had been a time of pure intrinsic happiness. Everyday life was spent doing chores, work and other duties, but now and again, if you were lucky enough, a holiday came along that enabled you to completely switch off and rewind, to a point of bliss.

It had happened in Florida.

November was an excellent time to go, and the weather had been superb. Every day, they sailed, moored up and swam, then rowed ashore to find an idyllic restaurant or food shack and eat seafood and the freshest salads and fruit cocktails. Her body felt thankful and her mind even more so. She didn't take her work phone or her iPad and had almost completely forgotten about Eden House for three damn weeks. Three weeks. It had been divine.

It could never last, that kind of perfection. Their relationship had been tested before they went, when Josie and Callum had witnessed their climbing instructor fall to his death. Kelly and Johnny didn't talk about it now. The holiday helped; they were grown-ups after all. Kelly's guilt over the accident was subsiding, and Josie didn't hold her responsible. Fortunately, Josie had never known about the whole thing being planned: the instructor had been a piece of a murderer's puzzle and Kelly had figured it out too late. She'd spent plenty of time beating herself up about being unable to save him. The killer had been drawn to the climbing centre because it fitted with their plans, and Josie had been caught up in it. Johnny had spent more time with Josie after her horrific ordeal, and she was undergoing therapy for her panic attacks. The funny thing was, for all the money spent on counselling, she was at her calmest with Ted.

Now, news was out about the murder in Potton Park, and Johnny said Josie was nervy. Like all woman in Penrith, young and old, she felt vulnerable in light of the shocking events. It made Johnny even more protective, and he'd texted Kelly a couple of times during the day to see if any progress had been made. Kelly thought about Thomas Watson's face. She had yet to meet the children. Of course, she would go to the funeral if Thomas approved. She always did. It would be a tough one: two teenagers. Christ.

Johnny smelled clean and welcoming. She was tempted to drag him upstairs with her, but she had little energy left, other than to eat and chug a glass of wine.

'Shit day?' he asked.

'Fucking terrible. The victim has two kids, aged fourteen and sixteen.'

'Jesus. I've been watching the news: there's a lot of scared women out there tonight.'

'Rightly so.'

'Is it true that the Beacon Estate is involved? Everyone is talking about gangs.'

Kelly was irritated, because the theory was derailing her focus.

'I don't know where that started; we have no evidence of motive yet at all.'

He put his arm around her. 'Come on, dinner's ready.'

'I need a shower.'

'Why don't you eat first? I'll get you a glass of wine and run you a bath.'

'You're spoiling me,' Kelly said.

Johnny went to the kitchen and busied himself with plates and cutlery, while Kelly sat down at the table and peeled off her vile tights: the worst invention in the history of agonising fashion choices for women. He placed a large glass of red wine in front of her, and she sipped it, closing her eyes and letting go. For half of the year, the four French doors to the rear of the property that led to the terrace overlooking the river were thrown open. But now, in November, they were shut tight, and it changed the atmosphere of the place. Bright, fresh and breezy was replaced with a cosy glow from the fire in the living room.

He placed a plate in front of her and she stared into a baked sweet potato stuffed with chilli and topped with sour cream and chorizo. She didn't speak for the next ten minutes. It was delicious, and she left nothing on the plate. She began to feel revitalised, and Johnny refilled her glass.

'Why don't you take that into the lounge and I'll call you when the bath is ready?'

Instead, she got a blanket and went out onto the terrace overlooking the River Eamont. She closed the door behind her and snuggled into the blanket, lying on a recliner, listening to the river and allowing her thoughts to return to semi-normal. When running a serious investigation, it was easy to let it take over and never touch earth, instead sinking further and further into the workhole, where she ate, slept and breathed the case. It was what she'd always been like before she met Johnny.

Light from the bathroom shone over the terrace and she stared into the distant blackness, trying to empty her head of images that shouldn't be there. She was jolted when Johnny called out of the window that her bath was ready, and reluctantly peeled herself away from the recliner.

The water smelled perfumed, and she stripped her clothes off in front of him and got in, sinking into the bubbles. He sat beside the bath.

'Wanna talk about it?' he asked.

She slid under the water, and re-emerged wiping her hair back and rubbing her eyes, smudging mascara everywhere.

'Can you pass my face wipes?'

He did so and she started cleaning off her make-up.

'It's early days. Ted reckons there were two attackers.'

She thought of Jordan and Millie Watson and how young they were to lose their mother. It was an unspeakable tragedy. No father ever expected to have to tell his children that Mum was never coming home. She thought of all the milestones in a young girl's life: periods, boyfriends, breasts, hormones, tantrums, make-up and waxing; all the things where you needed your mother.

It was heartbreaking. She missed her own mother every day. Moments came to her with searing agony, when she remembered a smell, or a song, or a birthday gift. Even after a year, it didn't seem to be getting any easier.

'God, I feel for those kids,' she said.

She slid under the water again. It felt cathartic chatting to Johnny about her day. She discussed all her cases with him. She'd never done that with a boyfriend before, except for when she'd dated a colleague, and that was rare. But Johnny took an interest. He was also hugely capable and intelligent, so sometimes she put a quandary to him and let him mull it over as if he were part of her team. It helped. He often spotted something that brought new energy to a case. She guessed that technically she shouldn't be discussing sensitive information with him, but it made her feel better and she knew he'd never tell a soul.

'Oh, this is bliss,' she said. 'I'm absolutely knackered. I went soft in Florida. What about your day?'

'It was pretty quiet, just one job on Haystacks.'

'Haystacks?' The peak wasn't difficult, but it was rocky. It was Alfred Wainwright's favourite and his ashes were scattered over Innominate Tarn at the top. It was about as peaceful a place as one got in the National Park. The view across to Pillar was jaw-dropping.

'You know at the top, where the craggy rocks jut up and down?'

She nodded. The walk followed paths all the way to the top, where a short scramble could catch a walker out, no matter what your level of fitness. The grey rock was unforgiving until you were over the summit, where it grew boggy again.

'A woman got her foot caught in a crack, and when she tried to step up, it twisted and she fell.'

'Ouch.'

'It was the nastiest break I've ever seen. She was in agony. The helicopter managed to get her from close to Innominate Tarn.'

Johnny had been with Cumbria Mountain Rescue for approaching eight years. He'd moved to the Lake District after a decorated career as an army officer. That was what had destroyed his marriage to Josie's mum. He didn't talk about it often, but he had told Kelly bits and pieces about tours in Iraq, Kosovo, Bosnia and Afghanistan. It was no surprise that he'd ended up somewhere quiet, isolated and beautiful. He looked like he'd always lived in the fells: rugged and strong.

'Are you on call tomorrow?'

'Yup. We both need an early night. I suppose you've got to keep your phone on?' he asked.

'Sorry. I'll understand if you want to go back to yours.'

'I'll call Josie to see if she's all right.' He left the room.

When she'd worked for the Met in London, Kelly could stay up all night figuring out who, where, when and why, but now she had found a renewed love of sleep, thanks to Johnny. They divided their time between his place and hers and when they were apart, she always slept badly.

She could feel her eyes drooping and the wine kicking in, and she reckoned she'd drop off quite nicely. She prayed that Penrith had a quiet night. If it didn't, she'd be the first to hear about it. She normally tried to ignore press reports, but the town was awash with them, speculating and frowning upon the sharp downturn in society's morals in the twenty-first century.

That was all bollocks as far as Kelly was concerned. People had been knifing each other since time began; the only thing that changed was access to information. Reporters stuck phones and microphones in her face all the time at crime scenes, but this was major news. The capital was seeing the highest knife crime rates since records began and the provinces weren't far behind. But no one, anywhere, had any solutions. The government said they were funding police to tackle it. The police said they had no resources. Community groups blamed the police. Politicians blamed the opposition. Parents blamed each other. Kids blamed adults. Schools blamed class sizes and lack of respect. Pupils blamed teachers. Everybody and nobody was to blame.

But still people kept on getting stabbed.

Kelly dried herself and put on a huge bathrobe. She heard music playing downstairs and felt lucky to be alive. She had survived so far, and she marvelled that fate had dealt her a fair hand up until now. As she rubbed moisturiser into her face and neck, and examined her new wrinkles, she reflected on the chances of someone born on the Beacon Estate escaping and making a different life.

It happened, obviously, but not enough. It seemed that kids were tethered to their environment for life and no one gave two craps. If lads from the estate did turn out to be responsible for the stabbings, how would society deal with them? Throw them away and fend off the blame?

Probably.

She had no idea what the ingredients were for happiness, but she was sure, from the monthly stats that flowed into her office, that on the Beacon Estate, right now, somebody was getting raped, someone's house was being broken into, a child was being filmed for a cheap porno, and a baby was being neglected. If she dwelled on it too much, she'd break.

She went downstairs and sat on the sofa next to Johnny. He'd got a fire going.

'Is Josie OK?'

'She's staying at Callum's.'

'Again? Do his parents mind?'

'They say they'd rather that than they sneak around.'

'Fair enough.'

They'd both met Callum's parents and they were good people.

'Would you rather have the TV on?'

'God, no, I don't want to hear about how fucked up the world is.'

He smiled. They listened to old classics from Moby, Coldplay and James Morrison.

Within ten minutes, Kelly was asleep.

Chapter 10

Jackson rolled over and looked at his watch: it was too fucking early. It was barely light and he realised that it was Thursday: he'd slept right through. He felt refreshed and decided to get up and make something to eat. He was constantly hungry. He stretched and put on a hoody, then went to the kitchen. He switched on the TV; the early-morning news was on.

He was just about to open the fridge, but stopped when he realised what the news segment was about. A woman was dead, stabbed in Potton Park yesterday. He wondered idly if it was a drug deal gone wrong. She could have been buying or selling, it didn't matter which. It was a fool's game. Jackson smoked the odd spliff and drank too much booze only occasionally, not wanting to let go, but it wasn't his life. Some people just got addicted and it overtook everything. He didn't like the way drugs and alcohol made his body feel: they sucked the life out of him and made a gym session disappointing.

He'd discovered the gym four years ago, when he was sixteen years old. It changed his life; gave him a purpose apart from hate, and focused his mind and his body. It earned him his nickname: 'Guns' Akers. It was why people left him alone; that and the knowledge that he was no threat. He didn't want to fight, that wasn't why he worked out. He listened as the newsreader said the woman was from the Ullswater area and had a family. It didn't add up. This wasn't some estate nobody.

He opened the fridge and found some roast chicken. He put water on to boil for pasta and checked his phone. He was ready for a training session, and the gym was only a ten-minute cycle from his flat. A message popped up, a request to make a collection, and he rolled his eyes. He rarely said no. He could be in and out in under ten minutes and still get to the gym before opening the garage at nine o'clock. That was where he fixed bikes. He didn't reply to the text: that wasn't how it worked. It was assumed he'd be there.

A noise outside caught his attention, and he went to the window to see what was going on. It sounded like a scrap, an argument. It was common enough to witness spats between teenagers, or worse, proper fights between rival gangs. But they rarely happened on the estate; they were usually carried out in previously arranged remote areas on the coast or down in Barrow-in-Furness. Members came in a steady stream from the villages and towns of the north of England: directionless boys, misunderstood and forgotten.

The closest rival gang was in Barrow. They were simply known by their family name, the Rawlinsons, and had terrorised the streets of the town for decades. Five of them were languishing at Her Majesty's pleasure for drugs and weapons offences. They carried on the business from inside the penal system, and word had it that they quickly became the top dogs there too. As a result of the incarcerations, though, the Rawlinsons had gone quiet, leaving the Cotton brothers, Jason and Adam, to strengthen their links to main players in Glasgow and Manchester.

Surprisingly, it was the brothers who were causing the fuss outside, along with Tyrone Fenton, a harmless enough kid who was Jackson's long-time buddy, and a few hangers-on. Tyrone was a good person, he just made bad decisions. It looked like they were arguing over a girl.

Jackson rolled his eyes: this wasn't going to end well. He was about to walk away from the window when Jason Cotton slapped the girl in question and she staggered backwards. He closed the curtains, but he could still see through the gap. He knew the girl. She lived in a flat in Wordsworth Towers. He watched as Jason Cotton tried to give Tyrone something, but Tyrone just shook his head. He appeared terrified and Jackson wanted to do some-thing for his friend, but instead, he continued to watch helplessly as Jason Cotton shoved Tyrone and the lad fell backwards. Meanwhile the girl was held as Jason thrust his fist into her time and time again. But Jackson soon realised that it wasn't just his fist.

He watched the girl fall, and the men, including Tyrone, run away.

He stepped away from the window and stared at the window. He swallowed hard and realised that his palms were clammy. He became aware of a bubbling noise and turned to the cooker, taking a spoon to stir his pasta, cursing when it stuck to the bottom of the pan. Whatever had just happened, he wanted no part of it. There was no helping her anyway. Jackson had seen enough people stabbed to know that the girl had no chance. Somebody else would find her and report it. She must have done something bad. Maybe it was debt. Maybe it was sex. Fact was, if you messed about with the Cotton brothers, you were nowhere close to being a nice girl. Playing with fire got you burned. It was a fact of life. But Tyrone had been part of it.

He ate his pasta, then went to pack his gym bag and left via the rear entrance. As he got his bike out of the lock-up downstairs, he heard screaming and assumed that somebody had found her. He looked at his watch: it was 6.15.

He cycled away.

In ten minutes, he was at the rendezvous point. He came to an abrupt halt when he spotted Tyrone, and thought about turning round, but then he saw his friend's face. He took a quick glance around and was satisfied that they were alone.

'What the fuck happened?' he asked. Tyrone seemed smaller inside his hoody, his face half-hidden. Jackson had his hood up too: it was standard practice in case anything went down, and it just had.

'You have to take this,' Tyrone said. He handed Jackson a black bin liner. 'Hide it.'

'What the fuck? Mate, you OK? You look like shit.'

Tyrone looked scared and shocked, and well he might. Jackson was sure he hadn't seen the hit coming: the girl was Tyrone's, and he knew he'd never hurt her, but she'd clearly done something.

He didn't let on what he'd seen. 'What did you do?'

'It's not mine.'

'Whose is it?'

Tyrone looked at him; he'd spent far too long there already. 'Jason's.'

Jackson looked behind his friend and saw the Cotton brothers sauntering towards them, faces, hands and heads covered. He saw no blood. It was Jason who spoke.

'No questions, Guns.'

Jackson took the package and cycled away, not looking back. He threw a glance over his shoulder and noticed a camera situated on the corner of a building. He hoped it was damaged.

Chapter 11

Kelly was woken by her phone at 7.30 a.m. Johnny groaned next to her. She sprang out of bed, hoping that it was a new lead. No one would wake her unless it was something important. Maybe they'd discovered some CCTV. She answered the call. It was the duty officer at Eden House; they'd received a call from a local squad patrol attending the scene of a 999 call: a fatal stabbing on the Beacon Estate.

It was the last thing Kelly expected to hear.

'Jesus. Fill me in, I'll go straight there.'

'Female, early twenties, mixed race, no witnesses, no weapon at the scene and no one's talking.'

'Typical. Address?'

Johnny rolled over and put his hand out.

'There's been another fatal stabbing, this time on the estate itself,' she told him. That woke him up.

'Christ, do you think it's a pattern?'

'I'll soon find out.' She bent over to kiss him. He held her, and she felt his warm body beneath her and wished she could stay.

'I'm going to have a quick shower,' she said.

'It's a big shower, I'll come with you.'

She thought about protesting, but Johnny knew the difference between making love slowly and making the most of an opportunity. They weren't about to break any records for tantric sex, but they both needed the connection. It was a good job she'd intended to wash her hair.

Twenty-five minutes later, she was on the road and using her blues to cruise through the traffic to Penrith. As a police officer, driving into any of the rough estates in Penrith was daunting. Beacon was the worst. She pulled a bobble hat over her wet hair and fastened her Rab jacket. The air was bitter, but quite a crowd had gathered in the early-morning light. It was a residential area, so this time there must surely be witnesses. But getting them to talk was quite a different matter.

The woman was still *in situ*. Ted was going to have a busy day. Kelly parked and showed her ID. Uniforms, on scene long before her, questioned the small crowd, as well as keeping an eye on any brewing trouble.

She went inside the erected tent and spoke to the CSI, who was sketching the scene.

'She was stabbed and left to bleed out,' he told her.

'Who found her?'

'A woman going to work at the local petrol station. The victim was unconscious by then, so we don't have a time frame yet. I'm assuming it was quick, given the amount of blood and the lack of rigor. Also the public location: she'd have been found quickly in the middle of a housing estate, where people are up and about getting ready for work.'

Kelly wondered how many people on the Beacon Estate were actually leaving for jobs, but left the thought alone. The location was less than a mile from where Ella had been stabbed yesterday. She'd have to consider if they were connected. It was easy to assume, simply because of the weapon, location and victimology: lone women.

Her phone rang and she looked at the name on the screen. Superintendent Ormond. Fuck.

'Kelly. Are they connected?'

'Sir, with respect, I've only just arrived on scene. I'm not making any assumptions.'

'I thought I could give something to Thomas Watson.'

'No, sir, I wouldn't do that at this early stage. The demographic couldn't be further apart. I doubt there's a link.' What the hell was he playing at?

'I went to see him last night. I promised him we'd have this wrapped up quickly. I'm glad he's agreed to do a TV appeal. Let me know the arrangements; I'll be there.'

Kelly rolled her eyes as she hung up. She wondered if Cumbria Constabulary, like the rest of the UK, had been given new targets to limit knife crime. She had no idea what they were supposed to do if some twat wanted to knife a woman in a park. The problem was bigger than telling kids not to carry weapons. They needed investment in education, housing, social welfare and community projects to tackle the issue. But that was all political, and way out of her control. Two fatal stabbings in less than twenty-four hours, though. No wonder Ormond was pissed off.

She turned back to the crime scene. 'ID?'

'Yup, she had a loyalty card on her for the supermarket on Bridge Street, 8 Till Late. Name's Keira Bradley. Address is up there, number thirty-two.' The CSI pointed upwards at the block of flats overlooking the scene. 'A woman in the crowd who was here before we erected the tent ID'd her and confirmed her address.'

'Right, I'll go and chat to her now.'

Kelly walked round the body. It was the second victim in as many days that she'd seen motionless and pale from blood loss. The woman's face was passive; her eyes stared dead ahead. She still had her handbag beside her. So not a robbery then. The bag was being photographed and searched; it was where they'd found the loyalty card.

'Ma'am.' Kelly glanced up to see who'd addressed her. It was the forensic officer who was going through the handbag. He held up a thick roll of banknotes and a small clear plastic bag containing dried herb: probably weed.

'How much do you think is there?' she asked.

The officer unfurled the notes and did a quick calculation. 'About five hundred quid, ma'am.'

'Bag it and tag it.' Couldn't have been a drug debt either.

Kelly went back outside the temporary tent and looked up at the flats. The line of sight was extensive. She counted at least twenty windows with a good view of where Keira had been stabbed to death. There were walkways, lift shafts and stairwells close by. She walked over to the uniforms taking statements from the public and asked if they'd had any witnesses come forward yet.

'No, ma'am.'

She'd experienced the same reticence before, in London, during her Met days. Sprawling housing estates, as tall as they were wide, all stifled by some silent code. It was almost impossible to find a snitch, and then to be sure they were a reliable one. It wasn't a good start. She understood that door-to-door information-gathering had already begun in Wordsworth Towers, the building where

Keira lived. A log was being compiled of all the properties and who lived there.

One of the uniforms pointed out the woman who'd ID'd Keira. As Kelly walked towards her, the woman looked nervous.

'You live around here?' Kelly asked. The woman nodded. 'What number?'

The woman pointed. 'Up there, number forty-eight.'

'So, near to Keira then. How well did you know her?'

'Kind of, not really.'

'Did she have a job?'

The woman laughed. 'Nah.'

So no explanation for the five hundred quid.

'Do you know how old she was? Family? Boyfriend?'

The woman looked even more fidgety.

'She had a boyfriend? Name?'

'Dunno.'

'Rumours?'

'Maybe.'

'We can do this the easy way and have a cosy chat, or I can take you in under caution as a material witness. You ID'd her; that makes you my closest associate at the moment.'

'Fuck off, man! You not taking me nowhere.' The woman backed away, but pulled her phone out of her pocket. 'Have a look on Instagram. You'll find everything you need right there.' She showed Kelly the screen and she made a note of Keira's Instagram account.

'I need to go.' The woman looked around, scared now. Two uniforms stood close by and she knew she had no choice but to cooperate. That didn't necessarily mean telling the truth.

'Did you hear anything?'

'Nothing.'

'Do you know anyone who heard something?'

'Nope.'

'Did Keira live alone?'

'No, her mam is ill, on disability allowance. She looked after her.'

'In the same flat?'

'Obviously, man. Jeez, you stupid?'

Kelly ignored the bravado. She turned away and spoke to a uniform. 'Has anyone been inside Keira's flat yet?'

'No, ma'am.'

'To inform her sick mother of her daughter's death?'

'No, ma'am.'

'Jesus.' She called Eden House to see if an informing officer was available. If not, she'd have to do it herself. The answer was negative. She grabbed a uniform to accompany her.

The stairwells were shabby and stank of piss. The doors to the flats were, by and large, dated and unloved. They came to number 32 and knocked. They knocked a second time, and eventually the door was opened. The woman could have been forty-five or eighty-five. She was ravaged by neglect and a poor lifestyle. A waft of stale air accompanied her and she looked puzzled to have visitors. She used a walking cane.

'I'm not buying nothing,' she said. Then she saw the uniform. 'What do you want?'

'We're looking for a parent of Keira Bradley. We were told that this is her address?' Kelly was struck by the contrast between this victim's home and what Emma and Rob had reported about Ella Watson's. It was as if everyone expected tragedy to occur here, but not to someone like Ella. It was jarring. She wouldn't say there was a nonchalance in the air; rather a sense of inevitability.

'What's she done? I'm her mam.' The woman leant on the door frame in a surly manner.

'We'll need to come in, Mrs...?' Kelly showed her ID and formally introduced herself.

'That bad, is it? It's that boyfriend of hers, no doubt. She wouldn't listen to me: always hanging round the bad 'uns. Come in, then.' The woman moved aside. 'And it's not Mrs nowt. It's Sharon Bradley.'

As Kelly stepped inside the flat, she had to give the appearance that her stomach wasn't churning in reaction to the range of interesting smells inside. There was cigarette smoke, body odour, questionable evidence of bodily functions, as well as animals. She heard scratching in a cage, and a cat sat lazily on a windowsill. Sharon Bradley limped to a chair. Kelly forced herself to sit down and concentrate on the devastating information she was about to deliver.

'Sharon, I've come here to give you some very bad news.' She kept the script factual; they always did.

Sharon eased into the chair and tutted.

'I'm terribly sorry to have to inform you that your daughter has been identified as the victim of a stabbing. A fatal stabbing.'

They waited.

The woman laughed. 'Are you pulling my leg?'

Kelly said nothing, just slowly shook her head.

'Where is she? Who says it's her?'

'A neighbour, and this loyalty card from 8 Till Late.' Kelly held the evidence up in a plastic bag so Sharon could see it.

'Where is she?' Sharon's voice increased in pitch and volume and she tried with difficulty to stand up. It was a shock response, and until the liaison officers arrived, Kelly or the uniform, who both had work to do, would have to stay and make sure she was all right.

It began to dawn upon the woman that they were telling the truth. The tears came, and Sharon's face was a picture of confusion and anguish, closely followed by anger. It was genuine emotion, and Kelly could see that despite the state of the place, Keira Bradley was loved.

'Oh God, I can't breathe.' Sharon was on the verge of hyperventilating. Her chest flushed pink and she repeated half-sentences as she slumped back in her chair. This wasn't the worst of it, though. Kelly knew that that would come after all the police, investigators, doctors, specialists and support officers had packed up and gone home, leaving the real grief to begin: the sorrow in the middle of the night that lurked in every thought and every face. The torture of losing a loved one through violence never stopped.

'Can I see her? Where is she?' Sharon appealed to the two officers.

'Do you think you'd be able to make a formal identification as her next of kin, Sharon? It would be at the hospital. At the moment, our inquiries are live and ongoing, and we need to gather evidence from people who might have seen anything.'

'You mean she was taken to hospital?'

'She died in the street, Sharon. I'm sorry. She passed away before the ambulance arrived.'

'I heard it! I thought it was the police. Any time there's trouble, I don't even look out the window. I could have...'

Kelly gave Sharon time. Then she continued to push little by little. She had to form a picture of Keira.

'How well do you know your neighbours?'

The woman reached for a handkerchief from the sleeve of her cardigan and blew her nose.

'I want to see her. I want to hold my baby. The neighbours? Why?'

'I know, Sharon. I'll make arrangements for you to see her as soon as possible. I'm asking because we're having trouble finding anyone who heard or saw anything like an argument or a mugging, or something of that nature. You mentioned a boyfriend?'

'Ding Dong, Dinger, something like that. He's bad news. Not a bad lad, but mixes with the wrong 'uns. No fucking surprise that no one's talking to you. You're hated round here.'

'I know.'

'You wait till I get hold of some of those kids who skate up and down and smoke their drugs. I'll collar 'em. You wait, I'll get a fucking queue of 'em to talk to you.'

They sat in silence. Kelly took stock of the woman in a fresh light, given her emerging grit. She no longer looked as unwell as she had when they first saw her. Sharon Bradley's hackles were up, and it gave her guts.

'Did she suffer?' Her voice was quiet.

'The medic told me that it was quick. The weapon hit a major artery. She would have lost consciousness almost immediately.'

Sharon wiped her eyes, then stood up suddenly. Kelly watched as she paced up and down. She didn't use the stick.

'Little fuckers!' she exclaimed, rushing to the front door. She picked up the cane and went outside, screaming at the top of her voice. 'You little bastards! You fucking butchers!'

Kelly and the uniform charged after her and found her leaning over the railing, waving the stick at anyone who might be able to hear her warnings.

'I'll skin you all alive! You!' She spotted someone walking down below. 'Tell ya fucking friends to find out who did this to my Keira, or I swear I'll get the lot of you!'

'Sharon…' Kelly began, but Sharon ignored her and made her way to the stairwell, banging on doors with her stick as she went, yelling threats and obscenities. She was drawing a crowd, and Kelly let her rant on. It was working; the woman was reaching more people – in more extreme ways – than the police ever could.

As she carried on downstairs, Kelly knew what was coming. 'Get in front of her,' she told the uniform. 'Block her from the tent.' He nodded and ran in the direction of the forensic tent. Sharon rounded the corner and the group of nosy neighbours that had begun to disperse stopped and watched the show.

'You!' she screamed in people's faces. Her rage was having the desired impact. Bystanders listened and reassured, promising to ask around. They calmed her down, and one woman invited her into her flat. Sharon agreed. Kelly went to her and gave her a card.

'I'll be in touch, Sharon. You'll be assigned a liaison officer.'

'Don't want one. I just want to see Keira. Wait a minute, is she in there?' She looked at the tent suspiciously. The woman who'd invited her in tried to hold her back, but Sharon shoved her off. People recorded on their mobile phones.

'It's a crime scene, Sharon, you can't go in.' Kelly blocked her path and Sharon crashed into her, bouncing back in amazement and confusion. A uniform arrived from nowhere and helped her steady herself. She got the message. The woman might have an enormous gob, but she wasn't getting past Kelly. There was also the CSI and a uniform at the entrance to the tent.

'Come on, Sharon, let's get out of here,' the other woman said.

Kelly watched as the pantomime drew to a close and Sharon allowed herself to be led away, exhausted, having vented her passion for now. It was a touching scene, and she felt powerless.

The crowd began to disperse as more officers arrived and imposed further perimeters. Kelly made sure that the scene was secure and went back inside the tent to start her own assessment.

'Overkill, ma'am,' said the CSI.

She went to him and knelt down next to Keira. The initial search was for evidence, weapons, a life-extinct verdict and a general feel for the layout, but now, having examined the body before it was bagged properly and sent to the mortuary, the medic had confirmed over a dozen wounds, consistent with what the police called overkill – or pure rage. That type of crime was almost always committed by somebody known to the victim: the complete opposite of the Ella Watson MO.

Chapter 12

The brothers swaggered towards the corner shop with a self-assured dominance. They flicked hand signals as they chatted and kept their hoods up. An elderly woman came out of the store and stared at them. She was at least a foot shorter than both men and her shoulders hunched over from years of gravity. She clutched two shopping bags closer to her.

'What's up, love?' Jason Cotton asked her. He opened his arms and stood in front of her. The woman tutted, and scuttled around him and away.

'Suck my dick!' Adam Cotton shouted after her. She picked up her pace. The two men laughed and performed some kind of fist ritual in self-congratulation.

When they went inside the shop, the proprietor looked up from his crossword and froze. It was that time of the month again, when the Cotton brothers wanted paying, but he'd never seen them so early in the morning. They looked high on something, and as if they'd been up all night. He'd toyed with calling the police, and he'd spoken to his wife about hiring his own thugs, but there was no getting around the fact that the brothers controlled the estate. His only option was to sell up, but no one in their right mind would buy. It galled him to the core that these two young men, who should be earning an honest wage from a legitimate day's work, exercised so much power. The tabloids had started reporting from estates where even the police wouldn't go: Beacon was one of them. He never saw patrol cars any more. The place was a lawless enclave of illicit trades and delinquency, and the authorities had neither the resources nor the inclination to care.

He didn't say a word as they helped themselves to crisps and bottles of fizzy drinks. They came to the counter and Jason, the elder of the two, leant over it.

'Get us two hundred fags.'

The man did as he was told. His profits were dwindling before his very eyes and he was being bullied into submission by a pair of children. His blood boiled.

'And the rest?'

He knew they meant money. He gave them five hundred pounds every month and it hurt his accounts keenly. He reached under the counter for the envelope, then stopped.

'What's up, old man?'

Under the counter, the man kept a hammer and a large mallet in case of burglaries. If he could have got hold of a gun, he'd have that too. He took one weapon in each hand and stood up.

'Get out of my fucking shop, you little bastards.'

The brothers burst into laughter and mimicked him. Adam lifted his sweater and the man saw a long knife stuffed in a kind of makeshift holster. Sweat formed on his brow, but he couldn't go back now.

'Get him, Adam,' said Jason.

The man moved first and he was quick. The brothers responded, separating, so that by the time the man emerged from behind the counter, he was flanked on both sides. Adam took out his knife.

'You wanna hurt, old man?'

'My CCTV is on!' the man shouted.

'We don't fucking care.'

As the man looked frantically between the two, Jason struck him on the head with a wooden club he'd brought out of his jacket. He went down like a sack of shit and the brothers stared at one another. Without speaking, Adam went to the office out the back and checked the CCTV monitor. He found what he was looking for and pulled it away from the unit in which it sat, removing the disk from the drive. When he got back, Jason was straddling the guy's chest, punching him in the face.

'Fucking hell, Jay, you're gonna kill him.'

Jason stopped. 'Nah, then he wouldn't be able to pay. Let's go.' He got up and stepped around the body of the man he'd beaten half to death. The man groaned, and they knew he was alive, for now. They cleaned out the till, then took the envelope and left.

As they walked away, they heard a scream from the shop: the old man lived upstairs with his wife, and she'd probably found him. Maybe this would teach them both a lesson.

'My fist hurts,' said Jason.

'No fucking wonder. You should have knifed him.'

'We don't want another fucker dying yet. The pigs are already crawling around.'

'Did you see Sharon Bradley on YouTube? She's a fucking nutcase.'

'Don't worry, she won't find nothing, and no one will tell her. Come on, we're late.'

They walked along swigging from their bottles, then threw them aside to gather with all the other bits of rubbish lying at the side of the road. They crossed to a dark alleyway and went into it. Beyond that was an abandoned industrial estate. It had once housed a paper factory as well as a shoe outlet. The buildings were in a sorry state, with doors missing and windows smashed. It was a favourite hangout for junkies, though not all the rooms were used by them. The smackheads tended to gather in huddles to keep warm, and it was the upper offices that they monopolised. The brothers headed for the car park to the rear, where a vehicle waited for them.

They didn't know his name, only his face and his voice. And his hands. They were always clean and looked mani-cured, and they stayed on the steering wheel. He never got out of the car; he just gave them verbal instructions and packages. Occasionally he'd accept a request from the brothers and say he'd look into it. But the relationship revolved around mutual convenience. The police stayed away from the estate, and in return, the brothers tidied up here and there. As they'd done with Keira Bradley.

'You fucked up, boys. Who killed the woman in the park?'

'What woman in the park?' Jason played the cocky ignoramus. Adam remained quiet.

'It's all over the fucking news!'

'We don't listen to the news.'

'Find out. She was jogging in Potton Park and she was stabbed to death. I want names. Coppers are going to be swarming all over this place, so you better be careful. Was it clean?'

'Yup.'

'Good. When you were told to make it two, you should have done your fucking homework. This changes everything. Take this and plant it on somebody, anybody; just get it done. Remember to unpack it carefully.'

Jason took a black bag from the man and shoved it under his jumper. The window went up and the car drove off. He used a different vehicle every time.

'Google that woman,' said Jason. Adam got his phone out.

'Fucking hell.' He read out the details and looked at his brother.

'Do you know anything about this, Adam?'

'What?'

'Don't fucking piss me around, fam. If you're involved, I'll fuck you over. I know that face. You better do as he says and get that over to Tyrone. Here.' Jason passed the black bag to his brother and walked away.

Chapter 13

The search of the pond in Potton Park was scheduled for
10 a.m., and Kelly decided that she might as well stay in
the area. The pond was a three-minute stroll from the tent
where Keira Bradley lay dead. Sharon Bradley's display had
hit a nerve, and the uniforms going door-to-door were
getting a more positive response than they had at first.
Everything was recorded to be inputted on HOLMES
later. Now she had two murder investigations running side
by side and she knew it'd test her mettle, as well as her
organisational skills.

Back at Eden House, things were moving in the right
direction. An old man had come forward to report that
he'd seen Ella in her car, and that she'd clearly been scared
by a couple of hooded yobs – his words – hanging around
the pay-and-display. CCTV footage was available for the
car park, and it had been confirmed that the unit was
fully functional, which was a result. The man was a resi-
dent of the Beacon Estate. Ted had left Kelly a message
late last night that Ella's autopsy was taking place this
morning. She called him and he'd already been informed
of the second murder. He confirmed that if the body was
released from the scene in time, he could autopsy the
second victim today also. On another note, he wanted
to know if Kelly would like to go to dinner at his place

with June and Amber, her half-sisters. Of course, Josie and Johnny were invited too.

She called the police underwater search team in Lancaster and they confirmed their schedule. Next she looked at the statement from the man in the car park and clicked on the CCTV footage sent to her by the data controller for Penrith Council. She saw Ella walk towards her car and felt a pang of grief for her and her family. She wondered how the kids were getting on. In the footage, Ella got into her car and two young men, their faces shielded, make sexual hand gestures to her. To Kelly's surprise, Ella flicked the bird at them and drove away. In his statement, the man said that the woman in the car, who he'd seen on the evening news, had made a rude gesture to him, but that when he saw the two young men, he understood why. Both of them were in hysterics. The footage could lead somewhere and needed to be followed through, but the two men in the clip were unidentifiable, due to their dress and the angle, so they'd have to rely on public witnesses.

Statements had also been taken from the Apple Store staff, where Ella had been before noon yesterday to get Jordan's phone fixed. The two members of staff who'd been on duty remembered her because the morning had been quiet. They reported no unusual behaviour or anxiety and said that she had been friendly and chatty.

Kelly sent an email to Kate Umshaw, who should be in the office by now, updating her on her movements. Kate could run the ship at Eden House in her absence. Rob Shawcross's task this morning was accompanying the forensic team to the Watson house. They'd been booked in this afternoon to search Keira's apartment too. Sharon

Bradley didn't mind; she had other priorities now, such as canvassing the entire estate.

After coming up to speed on her phone, Kelly watched as Keira's body was zipped up and loaded into a coroner's van. People were still on the streets asking questions and offering theories. The boyfriend seemed a popular one, but they had to find out his name. Somebody mentioned a guy called Tyrone. Information came in slowly but surely. She left the forensic team to tidy up and was happy that the perimeter was secure. It was time to go and meet the dive team, and Will.

As she walked in the direction of the pond, it struck her how close it was to Wordsworth Towers. She radioed the coordinator for the witness statements on the Beacon Estate and asked them to mention yesterday's crime during their inquiries to see if anything flagged up. If her theory was correct, somebody must have seen the perpetrators returning to the estate.

She saw Will in the distance, near the pond, and he waved.

'Morning, Will. Everything good?' She smelled a waft of Ralph Lauren and found it reassuring. She liked that he took care of himself. Though he was looking tired of late.

'Yes, boss. Always happy to be out of the office.'

'We'll let the others chew through the statements from the Beacon Estate for now. Do we know of any active CCTV cameras in the area?'

'I didn't go into Eden House, I came straight here, but I know there are plenty dotted around. Maybe we'll get lucky.'

'Something up?'

'No. Just a tough day yesterday. Looking at knife wounds is probably my least favourite part of the job.'

'Me too. It was a shit day. You not sleeping?'

'I'm fine, boss.'

Kelly left it and they walked in silence towards the underwater search team van, which had set up next to the pond. It hadn't snowed as forecast but the sky was heavy with promise. The pond looked uninviting; not that it was normally used for a pleasant dip anyway. It was the preserve of ducks, swans and litter, and was around three hundred metres long and twenty wide. Kelly had charted a route from the scene of Ella's homicide, taking into account that they knew from the two CCTV cameras that worked that the attackers hadn't fled through the exits. Instead, she concentrated her search towards the Beacon Estate, which was their biggest lead so far. That route passed the edge of the lake, where a person could dump a weapon before disappearing. She'd checked the area for CCTV and, as she'd expected, found none. She surmised that the attackers had made their decisions based on exactly the same criteria, which proved premeditation and some resourcefulness. It also meant prior planning and preparation.

The dive sergeant introduced himself and Kelly did likewise. He was dressed for dry land, and she guessed that somebody else was going in. The whole area had been secured, but they couldn't prevent people watching them from balconies and walls surrounding the park. She explained her theory to him, and they agreed that a strong man could potentially throw a weapon about thirty feet if he was running, or up to fifty walking. The speed and viciousness of the attack suggested that the perps would be running. The sergeant said he'd map out to fifty feet to be on the safe side. Kelly and Will watched as he charted a grid of squares over the area of the pond, and liaised with two divers readying themselves to go in.

Kelly had picked up a bit about diving in Florida. She and Johnny had done two casual aided dives, meaning they weren't qualified to go alone, but still they'd had to learn the jargon, and now she understood most of what was being said. She knew that the DV was the demand valve on the breathing regulator, and this was discussed a lot. It had to be tested before entering the water. She also understood that BAR was the air pressure left in the tank. She and Johnny had had to work out underwater how much they were consuming per minute and at what depth. They'd been so engrossed in their calculations that the instructor had to point out a grey nurse shark that had come to feed on the reef.

Key West was a far cry from the grey sky of Penrith and the murky brown water of Potton Pond. The two divers looked weighed down with equipment, and reminded her of other specialist departments on the force. They were muscular, focused and systematic and gave off the sense that one could trust them implicitly with the job at hand.

The dive sergeant explained what would happen.

'It'll be a fingertip search, as the visibility is so bad. Ponds like this are caked with bird shit and general rubbish. They'll split up and take half the grid each, like this.'

Kelly and Will watched as he pressed buttons and changed screens, checking the vital signs being sent by computer to his control room. It wasn't like a beach jaunt on holiday.

'They're going deeper than ten feet, so they're in full kit. We don't want to waste time.'

The two divers prepared to go in, and the sergeant tested their radios. He'd already taken a scan of the intended search area and Kelly looked at it with interest. There were peaks and troughs that she couldn't identify, and he explained that they were representative of the pond bed. He also explained that the true bed was probably under two feet of gunge, given his experience with ponds. They were used to plunging their thickly gloved hands into freezing cold mud, looking for sharp – potentially dangerous – weapons. A kind of underwater metal detector was attached to their search equipment, but Kelly knew that not all knives showed up on such gadgetry. At the end of the day, their fingers did the best work, but they were also the most prone to being sliced off by said weapons. The sergeant was well aware of what they were looking for, as were his divers.

The atmosphere grew tense as the gravity of what could be in that pond weighed on them. Kelly couldn't help but be hopeful, but in the same breath, she'd attended hundreds of crime scenes where evidence was found to be lacking, frustrating the whole case.

The screens beeped and they listened to the divers submerging. They had cameras on their heads and the gloomy world of the pond came into view. It was like watching the search for the *Titanic*.

No one spoke, though they could hear the divers' breathing. The radio crackled and the divers reported their findings. It was slow and laborious work as they pushed their hands carefully into lumps of mud, looking for indications of recent disturbance. They pulled out cans, chains, litter and toys and tried to lay them back down gently without disturbing the mud too much. Kelly noted that their breathing was much better regulated than hers when she'd seen that shark.

The sergeant checked their BAR, but they were so shallow that they both had plenty to complete the dive. Ghostly images came into view and Kelly wondered what attracted people to this particular job; she thought it grim, like being a miner, stuck in the airless dark.

The radio crackled again, and one of the divers reported that her metal detector was indicating something solid beneath her: it was a small object, the sergeant explained, judging by the sound of the alarm and the way the diver cast it across the area. She was instructed to search beneath the mud carefully. They watched as she tentatively sank her hand into the mud and probed, as if caressing a pet.

Kelly held her breath and squinted at the screen. The diver pulled something from the dirt and it kept coming. When the detritus settled, they could see that she was holding a knife.

'Yes!' Will fist-bumped the air.

'Submerged in no more than two centimetres of dirt, Sarge,' the diver reported. 'Looks like a recent dump: no corrosive damage and no adherence of organic matter. It's pristine.'

At the same time, the other diver's metal detector indicated another find. The same procedure was followed and the diver put his hand in where the detector was most acute. After a few minutes of gently delving, he pulled an object from the gloop. It was a second knife.

Will and Kelly looked at one another and slapped high-fives.

The atmosphere in the van was super-charged. Kelly knew that any team helping the police in a professional capacity wanted results, and they'd hit the jackpot.

'Shall I halt the dive?' the sergeant asked.

'I think we've found everything we're going to.'

'Right you are. Good job, guys, bringing you back in.'

They watched as the divers gave the OK sign and turned around. It was a short swim to shore and there was no need for off-gassing, as they weren't deep enough. They sat on a platform at the edge of the pond and took off their tanks and buoyancy aids, and Kelly and Will went outside to congratulate and thank them. They wore full suits because the pond was freezing and the amount of bacteria probably eye-watering, but they removed their gloves and shook hands.

The items had been carefully stowed in strongboxes, and they were handed over to Will, who took them to the van. Advances in latent fingerprint extraction on items submerged in fresh water had rocketed forward in the last ten years, to an extent where defence barristers had been rendered red-faced in court: the science staggered everyone.

They had something. They had more than something. The knives were different sizes and she'd know soon enough from Ted if they were a match. Now she had to get them measured, logged and sent over to him.

She paused for a second, watching Will, wearing gloves, transfer the items to evidence boxes. Two people had decided to leave home that day with knives, intent on bringing down an innocent victim. She might just be looking at the two weapons they had chosen. Were they taken from their mother's knife block? Were they newly purchased? Had they chopped potatoes with them to make chips?

She shivered and realised that she'd grown cold. She held out her hand to the dive sergeant to thank him.

'Glad to help,' he said.

As Will and Kelly walked back to the car, DS Umshaw called with good news: four CCTV cameras overlooked the part of the estate where Keira had died and the surrounding area. Footage was being trawled now.

Chapter 14

Ted Wallis had been the senior coroner for the north-west of England for approaching fifteen years. It was the type of position where one had to wait for one's predecessor to die. Now he knew why. There was no way he wanted to hand over the ropes to someone else, despite his advancing age. He was as sharp as ever (so he thought, anyway) and the work kept coming. One day he'd go into lecturing and touring, and perhaps even write a book: that was how most retired pathologists seemed to make their money. But he also had plans to spend more time with his family.

Neither Amber nor June had got around to having children, and it was something he regretted, though he knew they'd probably been put off the idea by his marriage to their mother. Mary was an alcoholic. Amber and June, looking back, had borne the brunt of her black-outs and had virtually brought themselves up. They were resourceful girls as a result, but he wished he'd spotted it sooner.

Wendy Porter had dazzled him in emerald green at a fancy ball thrown by the Earl of Lowesdale at Wasdale Hall on the shore of Ullswater. She'd been beautiful. He hadn't found out that he was Kelly's father until last year. And now he wanted to make the most of it. Part of that involved doing his job properly so she could do hers.

Funny, he thought, how he'd worked with her for two years before they found out her heritage.

The mortuary was peaceful, as always. It was a singularly still place, unlike any other he'd ever experienced. It wasn't for everyone, working with the dead, but it gave him immense satisfaction to tease out their secrets and perhaps even solve the riddle of their demise. He had several assistants who all performed different tasks. One took photographs, from angles dictated by Ted. Another handed him equipment, and measured and weighed. It was a smooth operation and there was no rush. There were no lives being saved on his slab.

He wore gloves for his own protection, not that of his patient. He positioned his microphone and tested it, satisfied that it worked properly, and began by logging the time. He was to perform the post-mortem on Ella Watson first. He double-checked her details with his assistant. It was protocol, to make sure they cut up the correct body.

He unzipped the bag. Samples of her clothes had been cut off and sent away in forensic packages. It was his job to remove the rest and discover what the police, CSI team and forensic experts could not see: micro fibres, hairs, residues and DNA material. Finally, he would delve deep inside the body, discovering what had happened to make the magnificent human organism expire. It took a lot more effort than people thought. In the movies, people got shot or stabbed and literally keeled over and died. It wasn't like that in real life. The human body was tough as old boots and took time to die. Snuffing someone out was no easy task. The bodies that graced his metal operating table were the unlucky ones. If the emergency services couldn't save you, then you must have been in a pretty bad way.

Ella's body was laid out on her back. She looked drained of blood, like the victims of old vampire movies. The bulk of it from the crime scene had no doubt been collected and swabbed, and the rest of it washed away from the road so that the public could enjoy the scenery without being reminded of what had happened there.

As he'd told Kelly at the scene, there were two wounds. Both were gaping gashes, with subcutaneous fat bulging from within, as was wont to happen with a live victim. Post-mortem wounds didn't bleed or split as much. He measured them both; as he had suspected, two different weapons had been used. He probed inside them, and found that both were longer than his finger could reach. He'd have to wait to see her organs to discover how deep the wounds went.

It had been a vicious assault. He could see, deep down, the severing of her femoral artery. It poked out into the wound like a plastic straw. The other wound was directly above her abdomen, where her aorta would be. It was a tragic coincidence and truly unlucky. The odds of two stabs slicing through two major arteries at the same time, from two different assailants and two opposing directions, must be a million to one. Those poor children had lost their mother in a lottery.

He turned his attention to her blood-soaked clothes. Swabs would have been taken at the site, but he put on magnifying glasses and searched for fibres. Locard's principle of exchange usually rang true, unless an investigation was particularly unlucky. Fact was, you couldn't kill someone without leaving something of yourself at the scene, as well as taking something away. Molecules were pesky little blighters that liked to latch on to the closest thing, both assailant and victim. A thorough hunt delivered. He found several fibres not matching Ella's jogging kit. One looked like a hair, and the others were all black and stood out on her blue running top: probably some sort of plastic amalgamation.

Satisfied with his inspection, Ted removed her clothes and carried on. Ella Watson had no other wounds or marks on her body. She didn't even show signs of having fallen hard; she must have collapsed pretty gently, with the weakness in her body taking over rapidly. Pooling had occurred all along one side where she'd lain until she was discovered. Death was quick, and his conclusion was exsanguination.

After just over an hour, Ted began to eviscerate the body. As soon as he pulled out the organ sac, he could see the aorta was cut in two. It would have spurted like a split balloon, explaining the amount of blood that Ella had been lying in when the emergency services arrived. He considered the way she had lain in the road and the direction of the strike, and concluded that it was possible the assailants could have got away without any obvious evidence of her blood on them. However, it was highly likely that they'd both received minute blood spatter patterns on their clothes and hands. Blood had a habit of travelling vast distances, as if the tiny cells colluded to form clues not visible to the naked eye to help catch the killer. Whoever had done this would have stained clothes. Not huge stains, but ones that would be visible in a lab. And the protein from blood wouldn't be washed out easily. It was something for Kelly.

After a thorough examination of Ella's internal organs, he noted that one of the stab wounds had travelled ten inches into her body and the other eight inches. They were not only very large knives, they were strikes of incredible force. The woman hadn't stood a chance.

He finished up and decided to have a short break. He was hungry and thirsty. Perhaps he was slowing down after all.

He sent his initial findings on Ella Watson to Kelly and told her he'd get started on Keira Bradley soon. She'd been brought straight to the hospital from the crime scene.

After a coffee and a raspberry Danish in the hospital staff canteen – both marked with red stickers to indicate that they were unhealthy – Ted stretched and made his way back to the mortuary to scrub up again.

Keira's body was different in the sense that the wounds indicated rage rather than speed. The amount of adrenaline required to fuel murder varies wildly. Ted was experienced enough to spot the difference between a pre-planned adrenalin-charged hit such as that on Ella Watson, and a split-second decision to lash out. For a start, Keira's wounds were mainly in her stomach, and numbered eleven in total. Kelly had told him that Keira wasn't robbed either; she'd still had a stash of cash and drugs on her. This attack smacked to him of panic, not the controlled power he'd seen with Ella. He reckoned it was an argument gone wrong.

Stomach wounds were generally the result of a lesson being taught to a rival or an inferior. In this case it could have been a man showing a woman her place. Ted confirmed that there was only one assailant and one weapon: a small, pointed knife, about six inches long.

Given that they were all anterior wounds, the attacker would have a substantial amount of blood spatter on him – or her – but if they were wearing dark clothing, it might not be immediately obvious. However, they would have a lot of blood on their stabbing hand, and perhaps even slashes as the knife became slippery with blood and the attacker lost control. Again, it was something for Kelly.

It was Keira's fingernails that caught Ted's attention. He gave them a good scrape and placed some of the matter in bags to be tagged, and some in test tubes to be cultured, then finally a sample onto a slide for his electron microscope. With a bit of luck, it wasn't just dirt and grime under there. Fingertips were generally hives of nasty bacteria, fungus and yeast. But with a victim of homicide, close attention was paid to what else might lurk under there. Ella Watson's had been pristine. That was not the case for Keira. They were stuffed with the normal keratin debris and skin cells found under dirty nails, so the chances of finding not only her own DNA but that of whoever she'd been close to in the hours before her death were good. He also found three hairs, deep in the hyponychium of two nails. Keira's hair was black, but the hairs were chestnut brown. Either her personal hygiene was questionable and she hadn't washed her hands for a long time, or she'd grabbed her attacker.

It took evisceration to discover which wound had killed her. One of the slashes had severed her inferior vena cava. She also had a ruptured spleen, pancreatic haemorrhaging and a damaged liver. She could have perhaps held on for the emergency services with a severed vein, but together with all her other injuries, unconsciousness and death, though not as speedy as Ella's, were inevitable in under five minutes without medical help. He'd read in her notes that she was probably found ten or so minutes after the attack. His conclusion was the same: exsanguination.

He felt dog tired, though he'd never let on to Kelly. It was a rarity that he had to perform two autopsies in one day, even in one week normally. That said, there was no way he would reconsider entertaining everyone tomorrow night. The opportunity didn't come around that often. He knew that June and Amber had great affection for Kelly. He hadn't detected a sniff of resentment from either one; in fact they had a lot in common: they were all strong women with definitive opinions they weren't afraid to vocalise, and they were all childless, for a start.

He was looking forward to seeing Josie too. Now it was time for him to prepare.

Chapter 15

Kelly and Will studied the CCTV footage when they got back to the office. There were two cameras situated not far from Wordsworth Towers and the data controller for Penrith Council had readily handed over the files. As expected, most of the male figures around the estate wore hoodies and bandannas covering their faces, but Will seemed to know a thing or two about the more prominent characters hanging about.

'When I worked patrol, I was partnered with my old schoolmate,' he explained to Kelly.

'You still keep in touch?'

'Of course. He ribs me about being out of uniform now and I wind him up about being still in it.'

'What does he do?'

'He heads up patrol for that area; he's Sergeant Liam Brook now.'

'Impressive. He must be good at his job.'

'The best. He's got plenty of informants, but not surprisingly, he's not that keen to hand them over.'

'I understand. It's tricky, but we could come to some sort of mutually beneficial arrangement.'

'That's what I said to him.'

'You discussed it already?'

'Kind of. These two look like the main players: the Cotton brothers. They haven't been round here long – they're from Lancashire originally – but they dominated pretty quickly, and they're fairly brutal.'

'How do you know all this?'

'Liam and I talk. He's my best mate. I'd die for him and him for me. We went through some stuff, you know?'

Kelly was taken aback by Will's candour, as well as impressed with his emotional disclosure. Not many men would readily admit this kind of respect and love for another man. She didn't ask what the 'stuff' was they'd been through together.

'So he gives you the low-down on the local thugs? Why are you so interested?'

Will didn't answer straight away, and she thought she'd leave it, not wanting to pry, but he'd stoked her curiosity.

'Can I meet him?'

'Of course. He's a top bloke. I know he's on duty today because he asked me to ring him when I'd looked at the footage. Can he see it?'

'Why don't you give him a buzz and see if he's free now?'

Will nodded and walked away from her desk with his mobile phone. Kelly went to check on the rest of her team, who were working tirelessly on leads for both murders. It had been a shock for everyone coming into work this morning to face a second murder. She'd briefed them about the coroner's findings when she and Will got back from Potton Pond. It was a double-edged sword of a meeting: on the upside, they had two knives from the pond that were being examined in the lab; on the down-side, they had two sets of perps, judging by the coroner's initial assessment that the MOs were too different to be connected.

Rob had come up trumps with his mapping of the area and was busy adding information to it. He showed her how it could be used with the whiteboard in the incident room. Emma was on site at Keira Bradley's flat, chatting to the forensic team, who'd finished at the Watson home earlier. Initial reports indicated that Ella Watson had been an average housewife who stuck to her routines and had no skeletons in her closet. In fact, she came across as too perfect. Two worlds had collided and Kelly could find no explanation for it.

Kate threw herself into the mammoth task of reading every single witness statement pouring in from the estate and the park, and deciding which nuggets of information to prioritise. She had at least three sightings of the Cotton brothers, and a statement had come in about a shop owner who'd been beaten up this morning, shortly after Keira's death. The wife of the man, who was still in a coma, had pointed the finger at the brothers.

Will came back into the office and told her that Liam was on his way. He was based with the drug squad on the other side of town. Drug crime was as extensive, if not more so, than all serious crime put together and tended to be investigated by an army of specially trained uniforms, with the support of patrol squads. Liam Brook had been heading up a unit over there for the past three years; Kelly had looked him up.

'Time for a coffee, then,' she said. They walked back to her office.

When Sergeant Brook arrived, Kelly was taken by his size. He was of similar build to Rob, but more than that, he seemed to fill the room with a sense of purpose to get things done. Will introduced them.

'I've heard a lot about you, ma'am.'

Kelly glanced at Will, who looked a little star-struck: he obviously worshipped this guy, and again she wondered what had brought them together and soldered the bond. She caught Emma gazing at the new arrival and smiled to herself.

Sergeant Brook had an open face and very large hands. She thought he'd rip her arm off when they shook hands, but in fact he was gentle.

'Nothing too bad, I hope,' she said.

'The opposite.'

'We've made coffee.' She left her office door open and they each took a seat. Kelly poured a cup of coffee for Brook.

'So, Sergeant, can you share with me what you know about the Beacon Estate?'

'Straight to the point. I've heard that about you.'

She saw Will watching them; he seemed amused.

'Call me Liam, ma'am, if that's all right with you.'

'And you're from a different unit, so you can call me Kelly.'

Will spread his hands, as if to register the injustice. Kelly ignored it.

'Where do I start with these lads?' Brook said. 'They've been at it for years. Our game is to clean up as much as possible without causing more damage, if you like. Sometimes it's easier to leave someone in a position of power and influence for the good of the entirety. It's a bit like communist Russia. Once it starts to crack, total collapse isn't far away. Our view is that if we keep a lid on the trouble, we can work with informants to catch the big fish and not waste time charging every Tom, Dick and Harry for stealing their mam's shopping.'

'I get the picture,' said Kelly.

'The estate has been run by the Cotton brothers for three years. Before that it was scumbags of a similar ilk, and we worked with them too.'

'You work with the Cotton brothers?'

'Not exactly. We gather information on them, and every now and again we find out what they know. For example, the busting of the Rawlinsons in Barrow came down to evidence supplied by informants.'

'Are they reliable? The Rawlinsons were rivals, weren't they, so of course they were going to testify against them.'

'But we had physical evidence too. With respect, it's a long-term project, and they have their uses.'

'What about the two murders?'

'I told Will, we've heard nothing that would have given the heads-up on either of those.'

'Can you bring them in and question them? They're implicated in a serious assault on a shopkeeper too: that's a legitimate start.'

'You need some leverage. If you concentrate on the physical evidence, I can work with my informants to give a fuller picture.'

'So you won't share your sources?'

'I can't do that.'

'What if it was the Cotton brothers who did it? Your empire stands to implode; who have you got lined up to fill the gap?'

'You're making it sound as though we run the estate.'

'That's how *you're* making it sound, I'm just curious about your relationship with these criminals. Is there an ongoing inquiry I don't know about?'

'There are several.'

'But you won't share that either?'

'Like you, we report to Superintendent Ormond. He runs the show. Only he can make that decision.'

'That's an interesting point. Did Will tell you that Ormond is pals with the first victim's husband?'

Liam shifted uncomfortably in his chair. He nodded. 'He's pals with everyone.'

'What's that supposed to mean?'

'Should we look at the footage?' Will interrupted them, but Kelly couldn't let it go.

'So how closely do you work with the super?' she asked.

'Too close.'

Kelly flinched a little. There was more than simply employee discontent in Brook's voice. There was real malice. Clearly she wasn't the only one Superintendent Ormond rubbed up the wrong way.

They watched the footage together. A man on a bike cycled into view. Liam rewound, stopped the film, scrunched his face, tilted his head and sighed.

'I reckon that's Jackson Akers.'

The clock in the corner of the screen gave the time as 6.28 a.m.

'Estimated time of death was between five thirty and six eighteen, when the 999 call was made. What's he doing out and about so early? He looks as though he's on his way somewhere.'

'He's got no record. Keeps himself to himself. He fixes bikes and the drug squad monitor him as a runner. It's part of a two-year inquiry. They leave him alone because they want to be led to the big boys. Possession and supply carry such small sentences now; it's the long sentences they want.'

'He looks relaxed,' Will said. 'Not as if he's fleeing a murder scene. He's more intent on that guy, coming into view.'

'That's Tyrone Fenton.'

'Tyrone? Is his nickname something like Ding Dong?'

'One of many. Apparently his old man was a ship's cook in the navy, in charge of the bell. Either that or Tyrone set fire alarms off at school. No previous, either.'

Kelly noted a change in Brook's tone but moved on.

'They look as though they're having a serious conversation. Tyrone seems nervous. Rewind it. Let's watch the whole thing again,' Kelly said.

They watched as Akers rode up to Fenton on his bike and they talked. Then a package was handed over.

'I thought drug deals were quick. They're obviously discussing something. Time?'

'Six thirty-three.'

'Wait a minute, who are these late arrivals?'

'Looks to me like the Cotton brothers. That one is Jason, the elder. The other is Adam. The rest are hangers-on.'

'Why do they always hide their hands?' Kelly asked, exasperated.

'They're copying American gangs: they cover anything that could potentially identify them – face, hands, hair…'

'So we have all your main players here in one piece of footage, potentially less than half an hour after Keira was killed, exchanging a package. That bag is large enough to contain clothes. Can you give me their addresses?'

'They have several,' Liam said. 'But of course I'll give you what we've got. I'll obviously have to clear it with Superintendent Ormond.'

'Really? I'm the SIO and this is a criminal investigation,' Kelly said. She was beginning to feel as though Ormond was guilty of being a bully.

Liam put his hands up. 'Look, you ask him. I have a hierarchy I have to go through for my own information, and it doesn't involve Serious Crime. Covert Ops and Drugs don't have the same rules as you.'

'What about the old boys' network?' She smiled.

Will patted Liam on the back as if to say *I told you so*.

'He said you weren't likely to take no for an answer. I'll have a few conversations this afternoon and see what we can do. Since I'm here, why don't you show me what you've got and I'll do anything I can to flesh things out?'

'Of course. Have you heard of the Bradleys? Keira was the second victim.'

'Yes. The family is known to us. I saw Sharon on the news, parading about. It was pretty effective, I have to say.'

'She could prove to be a valuable asset. I'll get DC Hide to show you around.'

Emma was more than happy to talk the sergeant through what they knew so far. After that, Kelly agreed that Will would accompany Liam back to his unit to ask a few questions. Maybe their friendship bond would work better than her charm.

Chapter 16

Superintendent Neil Ormond stared out of the window towards the menacing black rock of the peaks beyond the Penrith skyline. Yesterday the view had been marred by drizzle, but then that was what the Lake District was famous for: its unpredictability. He would have laughed at the irony had he not been so fucking outraged. The fact that the murder of a close friend's wife could happen on his watch, on his turf, and in broad daylight was beyond infuriating; it was embarrassing, and somebody somewhere was going to pay. It had been a gargantuan mistake to cut the patrolling of the Beacon Estate: the den of iniquity and dross that it had become. Work-shy lowlifes, benefit scroungers and drug addicts filled the lifeless grey concrete towers. None of them deserved the law to fall gracefully in support of those willing to defy it so brazenly.

His heart wasn't breaking; it had exploded. His anger was written all over his face, and people at HQ had avoided him all day. And well they might. Somebody's head was about to roll. But first he had to seek permission to shake things up a little on the estate. It only took a visit to the chief constable's office. She was the first woman to be cast in the role, and it galled Ormond. However, she believed in delegation and didn't micro-manage, so his division – Serious Crime – was left alone. The only time she'd stepped on his toes was when the press was breathing heavily on them to find a serial killer. It was only to be expected. She liked the camera and enjoyed giving press releases. She'd handled a school shooting back in 2013 and done a fine job of it, naturally commanding in front of the camera.

He argued that inaction might send a strong message to the population of the Beacon Estate that murder was not just acceptable, it was positively encouraged. She gave her blessing for him to go ahead with a series of raids on addresses across the estate, as a joint exercise with the drug squad.

He spent the best part of two hours designing the outline of a manoeuvre with the intention of smoking out the rats. It was time the network of coppers' narks got a shake-up. He spoke to the transport section leader in Penrith and there were enough vehicles to put together a sufficient number of personnel to go and teach the estate a lesson. Porter might be unhappy about the fact that two women had been killed by thugs intent on owning a part of Britain that had given up, but she would soon realise that her nose for investigating wasn't required in this situation. What was needed was somebody to make a statement; set an example. It never crossed his mind to inform her of his intentions.

He owed something to Thomas, and he owed it to Ella. The second killing had played right into his hands, proving that nothing would change unless they made some arrests and sent a message of zero tolerance to those responsible. The reprehensible monsters who'd murdered Ella had to pay, and somebody knew who and where they were. He'd had to stand in Thomas's house and admit that he hadn't been able to protect his wife because the Beacon Estate was lawless. It was shameful, and he wasn't about to sit here any longer and let it happen again.

The drug squad had its own way of dealing with issues: they sat and watched and did nothing, and it wasn't the first time he'd blamed them for a cock-up. He believed that if they did their job properly, all criminals would be facing charges, not just the ones they saw fit. The so-called sexy ones who grabbed headlines.

He put the last-minute touches to his plan and then beckoned the two officers into his office. Anyone listening along the corridors, or even outside, could be forgiven for thinking that someone was being beaten senseless. Ormond had learned to shout on the streets of Glasgow. He hadn't had reason to call on that particular skill for many years, but his bullish reserve sat just under the surface and he had no problem making his intentions clear.

By the time the two officers left, they were under no illusions about their objectives for the afternoon. Being old buddies, they knew exactly what the gaffer wanted. They were used to working directly under him, but they also harboured a deep distaste for the man asking them to head up what was essentially a hostile takeover.

'He's lost his shit this time,' Liam said.

'Did you notice that he made it all about Ella Watson and didn't even mention Keira Bradley?' replied Will.

'He doesn't give a fuck about people on the estate, just his own kind.'

'He can talk; he's as rough as they come. He was growing balls in Glasgow when people like the Watsons were cementing their future offshore wealth.'

'He's desperate to be one of them. Are you going to tell Kelly Porter?' Liam asked.

'I'm torn, man. I respect her. She's...'

'An innocent. I know, I see it in her. She fights for the underdog, doesn't she?'

'I'm not saying that she's never seen her own tragedy. She's got a hard side and she's got balls of steel, but she carries all this fucking hope around with her.'

'I know.' Liam smiled: it felt good to be in Porter's space. 'How do you work with all that positivity?' It wasn't a real question, more a statement of surprise.

'She believes in the truth.'

'She's fucking screwed,' Liam said.

'I dunno. She inspires people, I see it in the office all the time. Even when she meets a murderer, or a child abuser, they all diminish in front of her.'

'The second coming?'

Will punched his friend's arm.

'What will we do tonight?' he asked Liam seriously.

'What we always do: as we're told.'

'Aren't you tired of that?'

'We've got no choice.'

It was true. Since their first days on the force together, they'd been bound by events long ago that would forever dictate their futures. They were brothers in more than terms of camaraderie; they were bonded in experience and tragedy. Kelly Porter had no idea what Will's past horrors looked like, and nor would she.

'One day there'll be an opportunity to wring his neck,' Liam said.

'Stop it. I don't wanna fucking talk about it. Just do your fucking job.' Will's tone was sharp, but he hated the topic being brought up; it was in the past and would remain there. Liam had more of the scrapper in him, whereas Will was more rules-driven. Perhaps that was why they'd chosen their respective career paths: uniforms imposed the law instantly; detectives took their time. They both got there in the end. Of course he'd like to see Ormond get his comeuppance. But he was also a realist who knew that would never happen. Maybe that was why he had so much affection for Kelly: because she believed in the unbelievable.

Chapter 17

Liam drove Will in a patrol car to the other side of town, to a yard used by the Cumbrian constabulary to house its larger patrol, riot and transport vehicles. Will had been on similar raids before, without the knowledge of his boss. No one knew his marriage was over, and that he had time on his hands. He hated being at the flat on his own, so he tagged along on exercises like this one. When extra feet were required on the ground, his stellar history during crowd control exercises and on the street came in handy.

A fifty-strong task force had been given the green light to step up the rounds on the Beacon Estate. 'Step up' was an understatement. The order had come from Superintendent Ormond that vehicles were to stop and search any miscreants looking as though they were up to no good. It sounded vague but wasn't. Thugs and arrests were required.

The operation was coded Op Eagle and was designed to last for the best part of the evening, extending across the whole estate. They were to set up checkpoints and run a military-style zero-tolerance undertaking. Will felt slightly uneasy because he knew that at some point Kelly would find out, but, as he explained to Liam, their hands were tied. He'd take the flack when it came, and it would be worth it; rather that than tell her the truth.

He could hear her in his head and knew she'd lose her shit when she did find out. He knew how she felt about such draconian tactics. It was the worst kind of stereotyping: sending in the heavies to the underprivileged slum to weed out the baddies. But sometimes the rulebook didn't work, and secretly Will knew that his colleagues in riot and population control, as well as those in regular squad cars, wanted nothing more than to get their hands dirty getting revenge for countless victims. They'd all had enough. Enough of waiting around for the government to pour extra resources into ordinary policing. Enough of criminals walking free due to technicalities. Enough of estates like Beacon being no-go areas.

As he walked towards the depot, he felt something inside stir: a primeval need to seek justice. When he walked in and saw the set-up before him – officers kitting up in armour, checking helmets, discussing armed-response channels – and heard the low-level hum of anticipation, he knew he was amongst like-minded individuals.

They were briefed at 4 p.m. It was already dark. Raids were usually carried out either before dawn or after dusk, to exploit the element of surprise. They listened to last-minute instructions and checked equipment. Detectives often had to prepare for dangerous exchanges, and their training in basic defence weaponry had to be kept up to date. Will weighed the heavy truncheon in his hand. It felt good.

He looked around and wondered where Superintendent Ormond had got the manpower from so quickly. He was a man on a mission; everyone knew that he had a personal interest in the case. Well, in as much as he rubbed shoulders with the wealthy Watsons. He had already made it clear that Keira Bradley wasn't the motivator here. That was the irony, and Will knew it. It had taken the death of a rich white middle-class woman to stoke the fire.

The atmosphere was testosterone-charged, though Will spotted a decent number of women. They had the same look about them: hunger. He smiled. He'd done the right thing. He thought about his boss and how she might react when she heard the news, and discovered that he'd been involved, but he had his story ready. He'd say they'd needed as much manpower as possible, and that it was a direct order from the supervising officer. It bugged him that Ormond hadn't involved the investigating team; it should be a joint operation. But he knew why the super wanted to act alone: because his ego was getting the better of him and Kelly Porter saw straight through it. He also knew that, of anyone on the force, Kelly would discern the real motivation behind Ormond's fervour to get the case closed quickly.

The final command to load the vehicles came in, and Will followed Liam into the back of a large van. It held around fifteen of them. Further sitreps and operational commands would be delivered en route. They'd been cleared to arrest at the first sign of trouble or lack of compliance. As they set off, the tension inside the van was palpable. The officers glanced at one another or chatted quietly. Will saw that they were part of a convoy of around seven vehicles.

Back at the office, his colleagues would be working intently on the finer details of the case, crunching data and staring at computer screens. He missed the streets and this was one way to scratch that itch. Maybe they'd bump into Tyrone Fenton tonight. He hadn't told Kelly that the reason the shithead had no record was because three years ago Liam had beaten him half to death and got away with it. Will had helped fix the evidence. Fenton's file had been cleared as a result. The kid never squealed, and Liam ended up behind a desk for a year.

Adrenalin spiked as they neared the entrance to the estate. The high-rises loomed sinister and forbidding. The vehicles stopped abruptly and the back doors were flung open. Will stuck to Liam's side. They were to patrol on foot and question anybody looking suspicious or loitering where they shouldn't. Will could see a group of youths in the distance wearing hoods and scarves over their faces, a fashion statement that had been imported from US prisons, along with wearing jeans below the pant line because belts weren't allowed in jail. It was a sad indictment of society when role models were felons. Artists and hangers-on covered their faces on drill-rap videos for fear of being identified and stereotyped. He'd watched enough of them to know the two went hand in hand: criminal gangs and explicit, violent rap music. Drill culture was infecting youth on an unprecedented level. Sure, there were outreach centres full of do-gooders willing to donate time and money to rehabilitating these young offenders, but it wasn't enough. Who wanted to trade status, cash and easy women for meditation, penance and volunteer work? No one: that was the answer.

Jackson Akers' flat was in full line of sight to where Keira Bradley had been butchered, and they wanted to ask him what he'd seen. They also wanted to know why he'd been so busy around the estate on his bike earlier today. They headed towards Wordsworth Towers. The estate was fairly quiet, but word of the police presence was already getting round, and it seemed from what Will heard on the radio channel used for the evening's events that people were doing the opposite of what Ormond had expected them to do: they weren't staying indoors, they were coming out onto the streets and balconies and questioning the police directly. This called for a different skill set entirely, and Will could hear officers engaging in Q&A sessions. It was wholly unexpected.

On the balcony overlooking the spot where Keira had died, a group of people, all ages, bombarded Will and Liam with questions. They demanded justice for Keira, they asked why the rich white woman mattered more than a mixed-race one or a poor one. They wanted to know how the police were going to protect their community. Tension ramped up, but the two officers answered as best they could and calmly explained that they were visiting properties pertinent to their investigation. They made it clear that they were only interested in anyone not complying with the law.

'Let 'em do their job.'

It was Sharon Bradley who spoke. The small crowd parted.

'It's Akers you want to see, ain't it?' she asked. The crowd looked from her to the cops. Silence descended.

'We're on our way to the address of Jackson Akers, yes, ma'am. We're sorry about your daughter; we're trying our best to get answers.'

'He's a good boy. Mind you don't go too far with your interrogation.'

'It's simply important to our inquiries, ma'am.'

'Pig.' Spittle flew from nowhere and landed at Liam's feet.

'Now we'll have none o' that! Shut the fuck up and let 'em do their job, I said.' Sharon's authority overwhelmed the crowd again and they fell back. Will saw that more figures had appeared on the balcony. It seemed like half the estate was out.

'I'm coming with yer,' Sharon announced. Liam rolled his eyes. 'I saw that!' she admonished him.

She followed them to Jackson's door and waited. After a few seconds, the door opened and Jackson registered his visitors and the people on the balcony.

'You'd better come in,' he said, nodding to the spectators.

'Show's over, give 'em some peace,' Sharon instructed. 'Guns, you want me to come in?'

'Nah, Shaz, safe.'

Will and Liam entered the flat and Jackson closed the door behind them.

Chapter 18

Across the estate, a group of three uniformed officers banged on Tyrone Fenton's door. No one was home.

Superintendent Ormond gave permission for them to smash the door in, pending a warrant. It was received ten minutes later, and one of the officers stepped forward with a battering tool, taking the door out with one resounding crack. On entering, they found the usual waste associated with drug abuse and idleness. The air was thick with stale smoke; the place had obviously been vacated recently. Ashtrays full of needles, spoons, foil and brown goo were everywhere. Clearly the flat was not a home but a drugs den. It was confirmed empty and sealed off, waiting for a forensic team to sift through the dregs.

Over the radio, reports were growing in number and urgency of disturbances across the estate. Outside Tyrone Fenton's flat, shouting drew the officers to the stairwell, where a crowd of around thirty residents surrounded four colleagues. The situation was escalating quickly. No one had anticipated the level of anger being displayed. They'd expected everyone to stay indoors, as they did ordinarily when police patrolled. A gathering of such size on the estate had never been witnessed before, and it was clear that this wasn't an isolated incident. Suddenly all the residents of Beacon wanted to have their voice heard. The police had woefully underestimated the scale of defiance. Op Eagle was falling apart. Officers communicated their critical assessment over their radios, but no one seemed to be commanding the operation centrally. There was no clear strategy on how to withdraw. It hadn't been discussed.

Superintendent Ormond had not changed the orders and the commander on the ground was left to make the decision to pull the plug. What had started as a multi-locational display of control was turning into a mass protest, and they weren't equipped. The radio crackled with requests to regroup and bring Op Eagle to a close for now, perhaps regaining a foothold after things had quietened down. Questions were heard flying back and forth; confusion was setting in. Individual pods of officers decided to follow their original orders and make their way through the streets, stopping and questioning groups of people; others abandoned the brief and made their way back to the vehicles.

Finally a decision was made and it was communicated to all officers that Op Eagle was being suspended. The new objective was preserving the security of personnel. The search for the Cotton brothers was called off and the officers prepared to get back into their vehicles. Overhead could be heard the whir of a helicopter's blades. Police choppers carried infrared cameras as well as equipment for thermal imaging and long-range stills. They could track anybody who moved and record it in real time. It was a warning to the community of the Beacon Estate to step down.

A head count revealed that all officers were present apart from two pairs. As they were loaded onto the vehicles, things grew ugly. The crowd swarmed and shoved, and someone threw a bottle, which smashed on the bonnet of a van. The doors were locked and word came through that Superintendent Ormond had given Armed Response the go-ahead. Officers kept their heads down and clung to seat backs as their vehicles shook with the sheer force of the crowd. Finally they were moving. One van and a squad car headed to the playground where two colleagues were surrounded, and the rest of the vehicles were told to rendezvous at the entrance to the estate and wait. The sounds of a mob gathering could be heard crackling over the radios. Officers bit their nails.

'Op Eagle vehicle 247 approaching south playground. Approximately one hundred agitated residents, all ages. Repeat, approximately one hundred agitated residents. Situation critical.'

The vehicles bumped over the uneven roads and the atmosphere was charged with electric tension. The shouting at the playground was still at a level that, with experience, could be classed as non-threatening, but the number of officers present versus the size of the crowd made it a grave state of affairs. The order came through for the rest of the vehicles to divert to the scene. Resources were diverted to the growing crowd at the playground.

It seemed to take the convoy hours to get there, but it was in fact only around three minutes before they pulled around the corner and spotted the children's play area, overrun with angry residents of all ages, some old, some young; children as well as families. The real concern was that they couldn't see their fellow officers.

A warning was shouted from somewhere in the crowd, and suddenly the mob began to dissipate as if a bomb had gone off in the middle of them. Officers fought their way against the tide of residents eager to get away. People jumped the railings and others filed out of the three gates. A great roar rose and the crowd began to run. Children were trampled and women screamed. Officers had no idea whether to make arrests or save the people being crushed. It was a disaster. No one knew who'd caused the panic. Men in masks and hoodies slipped away, protected by women and children.

Three armed-response vehicles turned up and officers spilled out of them, weapons cocked and shouting warnings. The few people left in the play area froze and held up their hands. Some dropped to the floor, and were quickly apprehended with cable ties and handcuffs.

In the middle of the playground, slumped next to the sandpit, were the two officers who'd been left isolated in the enormous cock-up that was Op Eagle. In fact, it would come to be known as Op Turkey. As a few stragglers were arrested and scuffles broke out in the surrounding streets, the pair were attended to by their fellow officers.

One was unresponsive. The other's head lolled on his chest. Both had been badly beaten. Despite working with them on squad patrol for the past five years, the two officers who were first to attend them could only identify them by their numbers on their lapels.

'Officers down! Get a fucking ambulance!' one screamed into his radio, spittle landing on his friend.

Chapter 19

Sharon Bradley let herself into her flat.

She was exhausted. Her body ached, she was emotionally numb and she needed a break. She'd been going all guns blazing since early this morning, purely on emotional charge, and now she was empty. She'd done all she could to bring Keira's murder to the attention of the residents of the Beacon Estate, but she feared that the genuine concern she'd raised would only last a day or two, if she was lucky, before everybody got bored and forgot about her daughter, unlike, she suspected, the death of the posh woman. But for now it was something to focus on and keep her busy. No one could quite believe the audacity of the police, marching in like that, thinking their uniforms and bullying tactics would get them the results they wanted. People were more likely to protect those who'd murdered Keira now. Sharon's hopes of encouraging witnesses to come forward faded and she felt a deep melancholy.

Away from the chaos of the night, caused by the frigging bastard police, who'd thrown their weight around rather than search for the killers, the peace of her flat was welcome, but also a reminder that Keira wasn't coming through the door ever again.

They'd had their fights, like any mother and daughter. Keira could be a handful. She'd been an independent gobshite all her life. Life. No more life.

Sharon picked up the post and dropped it on the table. The coppers had been in her flat for most of the day, searching through Keira's personal stuff for clues. She reckoned if they were going to find anything it would be on her phone; the girl had lived on it. She went to her daughter's room and opened the door, holding onto it, frozen on the threshold. She could hear shouts and screams coming from outside, faint now and sporadic, unlike earlier, when the streets had been a virtual war zone. Her vision of bringing the estate together lay in tatters on the roadside.

The window was open a little and the nets billowed inwards on the breeze. The wallpaper was torn in places and hadn't been changed in years. Sharon only noticed it now and wished she'd redecorated the room for her daughter. The police had been respectful and everything was in order. She'd told them to take what they needed. What did she want with a load of hair gel, ghastly make-up and miniskirts anyhow? But now she found herself wanting to touch everything. She sat on Keira's bed and picked up a mirror. She had no idea where it had come from and realised with a shock that she knew little of her girl's life behind this door. Keira had always been fiercely private. Sharon only really came in here to pick up clothes or tell her that her tea was ready. She tried to recall a routine, a semblance of what they shared together, but she found little in her memory to hang to and say that's how it was with her daughter.

She lay down and buried her face in Keira's pillow. Her scent was still fresh. She closed her eyes and remembered the day she'd given birth to her. Of course, the father was nowhere to be seen; he'd fucked off months before. It had hurt. The birth, not the desertion. She'd huffed and puffed and suffered in agony for twenty hours before they gave her an epidural, which didn't work, so she screamed some more. She'd felt as though her fanny was exploding. The downward pressure of what felt like a red-hot rock would be burned into her memory forever. Keira had been her only child.

She lay curled up in the foetal position for many minutes with memories of her baby. She knew that the papers would report Keira's death very differently compared to that of the woman from the big house on Ullswater. She knew that value was all about money. Keira hadn't had a job, though she'd done the odd shift here and there. She hadn't done well at school and was always in trouble. Rich folks didn't realise that if you were born into shit, it was almost impossible to climb out of it.

Her throat was hoarse from all the shouting. It was her way of coping. But now, alone and having to face her worst nightmare, she couldn't manage to battle through the fog; it just kept drenching her with its murky mist.

She didn't know how much time had passed before she finally got up to answer the door, and she'd never appreciated the compassion of her neighbours until now. Two of them stood there expectantly, and she invited them in. She made tea and they talked about the police raid. She sifted absent-mindedly through the mail as she waited for the kettle to boil, and reassured the women that she wasn't about to top herself, though she felt like it occasionally, when the pain hit her. She opened a letter and stopped.

'That's odd.'

'What's odd, Shaz?'

'Keira had an appointment with a fancy solicitor in Manchester booked in for next week.'

'What about?'

'It don't say.'

'Ring 'em.'

'They'll be closed.'

'Tomorrow!'

'I will.'

Chapter 20

At Eden House, Kelly was busy examining the CCTV footage and the information given to her by Sergeant Liam Brook. She was working on an action plan that was standard in scenarios where multiple suspects needed questioning: split them up and conduct the interviews simultaneously across multiple sites in the area. It was a proven technique to get conspirators to rat each other out, though sometimes, like in the Stephen Lawrence case, they blamed each other to such a convincing extent that they confused a jury and escaped conviction. Which was why it had to be planned meticulously.

She hadn't seen Will all afternoon, but trusted that he was unearthing some nuggets of gold for their inquiry, with the help of Liam Brook. She liked Liam. He reminded her of her father – or rather, the man she'd called Dad for over thirty years. John Porter had been a reliable bobby, and risen to the heights of sergeant, like Liam. They were both tall, broad men with steely eyes that were also soft. She could see that he had huge affection for Will, and that made her like him even more.

Ormond wasn't answering his phone.

The two men who'd earned the finger from Ella Watson before she'd headed off for her run had been brought in for questioning, but they'd turned out to be a mere momentary glitch in her afternoon: both had alibis that checked out for the rest of the day. They were guilty of indecent behaviour, not murder.

The old man who'd reported them turned out to be a mine of information and shared it with them readily. The death of the woman who'd inadvertently given him the bird had affected him profoundly, and he wanted to do all he could to help. He told them that he'd spent years watching the couriers coming and going, and knew which flats they went into and who he suspected of being responsible for grooming youngsters into skipping school and turning bad. He was like the guardian angel of the estate and he never stopped talking, giving them names associated with their current lines of inquiry and addresses where he'd seen the Cotton brothers hang out. The only downside was that Kelly's team would have to follow every one of his leads, even if it turned out to be pure sour grapes or poor memory.

Kelly was ploughing through HOLMES. As information came in to the incident room, it was uploaded onto the IT software. Its compatibility across all county constabularies in England, Wales, Northern Ireland and Scotland, as well as the Royal Military Police, made it uniquely invaluable to any major investigation. A question could be put to the database and answers, in order of relevance, would be forthcoming in minutes. It was like having two hundred extra officers working in the incident room. For officers like Emma and Rob, it was a wet dream. Their analytical skills were constantly being pitted against the machine, and sometimes they beat it to conclusions. It was something of an office challenge.

They all needed their light relief.

Statements from witnesses flooded in from the Beacon Estate, and every one of them mentioned that their stimulus was a word from Sharon Bradley. This could be a double-edged sword: testimony that might prove crucial at trial could be made to look like coercion of a witness by the victim's mother. It was emotive stuff and utterly biased, thus useless in court should it be their only evidence. All the statements deriving from Sharon's network on the estate would have to be verified by independent sources or scientific fact.

Sharon was doing a fine job of bringing an end to her various disability benefits as she whirled around the estate drumming up momentum for their inquiries. Kelly had found out that she had been in a horrific car accident several years ago and had used a stick to walk ever since. Though Sharon's new purpose in life had given her more vigour, Kelly wasn't about to report her as a benefits cheat; the woman had had it rough.

Rob disturbed her train of thought.

'Boss, reports are coming in of an organised police raid on the Beacon Estate. By all accounts it's chaos down there.'

Kelly couldn't believe what she was hearing.

'I've googled it and it's all over social media,' he said. 'Look.' He linked his computer to the whiteboard, and clips, videos and news items came up on screen. The TV in the incident room was on silent for most of the time, when they were ordinarily going about their daily tasks, but when a major inquiry caught the attention of the press, they turned it up. Rob switched to local news, and sure enough, the raids and arrests on the estate were being reported.

'Jesus,' Kelly said.

More officers came into the incident room and they watched in amazement as events unfolded. Much of the footage looked as though it had been shot on mobile phones and showed terrified residents running away. Images from an overhead helicopter revealed a large crowd surrounding police.

'Who authorised this?' Kelly was fuming. She clenched her fists and an uneasy feeling settled under her ribcage. She knew the answer before Rob confirmed it with a phone call.

'Op Eagle was authorised by Superintendent Ormond, guv.'

Kelly marched out of the office and dialled Ormond's number furiously. She barely let him finish his formal greeting.

'Sir, I'm hearing reports of a disastrous operation on the Beacon Estate of which I had no knowledge.'

'Yes, Kelly. It was purely an operational pincer move-ment to garner more information. Unfortunately, a mob gathered and our officers were quickly outnumbered.'

'Sir?' Kelly's blood boiled.

'Armed Response defused the situation and we've made several arrests. We were after certain characters asso-ciated with the gang responsible for the most serious crime in the area. In fact, we think—'

'With absolute respect, sir.' Kelly spoke with her teeth locked together. She felt like punching him. 'With respect, sir, I'm the SIO on this case. I could have given context. Which characters exactly?'

'I don't know names; you'll have to talk to the operations sergeant. They were supplied by reliable intel from drug surveillance.'

'Drug surveillance, sir? These are suspects likely to have committed both murders. We've been examining CCTV all day and now you've gone and thrown me under a bus.'

She remembered who she was speaking to and closed her eyes. Shit. For the first time since she'd been back in Cumbria, she regretted her decision to leave London. This was a man twenty years her senior in experience, and now she wondered how he wiped his own arse. Was it still possible, in 2018, to have such incompetence on the force? His arrogance staggered her.

To her amazement, he didn't reprimand her. He was in too deep because of his relationship with the Watsons. She realised she felt sorry for him.

'Sir, could I have the name of the operations sergeant in charge? I need to correlate Op Eagle with my own investigation. I can't work on the periphery.'

'I agree. It was supposed to be helpful. I don't know what went wrong. I'll take full responsibility.'

'Is it true that we have two officers in hospital?' Her voice was heavy and it took every ounce of strength not to call him a fucking muppet.

'Sadly so, Kelly. They were beaten. Armed Response was called too late.'

'Will there be an inquiry, sir?'

She heard a shift in his breath and could have kicked herself. She needed to be careful. Ormond was still top dog around this place and she was a mere DI. She heard him cough.

'I think we'll leave it there, Porter. Don't forget that I still choose the SIOs around here. I might not sit next to your desk, but I know everything you do and it's my impression that you've taken more than a few risks during certain investigations.' He hung up.

She stared at her phone.

She'd screwed that up royally. There was only one way to regain some ground, and that was to find out exactly what had happened on the Beacon Estate. Should she have to go head to head with Ormond in the future, she wanted her facts straight.

She marched back to the incident room and spotted Will.

'Will, where have you been? Christ, you look like shit. Sit down.'

'I've been at the Beacon Estate, boss.'

'What? Were you caught up in that raid?'

'Yes, ma'am, I had no choice. They needed every pair of boots they could get. I volunteered.'

'Without telling me?'

The officers on Kelly's team all stopped what they were doing and stared at DS Phillips, then at their DI.

'And your rationale for bypassing me was what exactly?' She'd forgotten where she was and that she had an audience, but a cough from Kate reminded her. She stared around at all the expectant faces. Her glare was enough to make everyone move away, and she turned back to Will. 'My office.'

She walked away. Will followed. She held the door open for him, and when he was inside, she slammed it shut. Everyone went back to work.

'I need you to tell me what the fuck just happened, Will. I've got Ormond tearing my investigation apart and obstructing me at every turn because he's involved personally. And now you've publicly betrayed my trust!' Her voice broke. It was a wounding treachery. She leant over her desk, spreading her arms and staring at him. Will stood in front of her, anguish all over his face.

'It was an order, ma'am.'

'By whom?'

'The super, via Liam.'

'Why?'

Will bit his lip and Kelly studied him closely. The man was in turmoil. What was he hiding?

'Will, what's going on? I've never known you behave like this. Why did Ormond make such a rash decision? It's all gone tits-up; it was a folly on a gigantic scale. Did he get it past the chief constable?'

'Yes.'

'How the hell?'

'He's very convincing.'

'I can see that! This derails everything we've done so far to finally break down some barriers on the Beacon Estate. It makes us look like fools!'

'Ma'am—'

'Call me Kelly, for Christ's sake, Will. We're behind closed doors.'

'Kelly, I…'

'Tell me! What is it?'

'I can't.' He sat down heavily and put his head in his hands.

Kelly was taken by surprise and utterly confused. She also sat down and reached across her desk, placing her hand gently on his arm.

'Will? What is it? Is it that Ormond doesn't think I'm getting answers quickly enough? Is it his friendship with Thomas Watson?'

'I think he thought he could pull it off and look the hero.'

'But you didn't believe that, did you? What about Liam?'

'It's not easy for me and Liam to disobey orders. We came from a place we don't talk about. Ormond has been telling us what to do our whole careers. When you arrived, I thought it would all be different. And it is! You're not in his pocket at all, and he hates that.'

Kelly thought about what Will was telling her and it made her confusion even worse.

'Who the hell is in charge of this investigation? I need to be sure of my position and your loyalty. I'm forbidding you to have direct contact with Superintendent Ormond without going through me, do you understand?'

He laughed, and Kelly pulled her hand away.

'You have no idea what you're dealing with, do you?' he said.

Chapter 21

Jackson's brow was covered in sweat. Since the coppers had left, he'd been pacing up and down trying to make a decision. He kept looking out of the window from which he'd seen Keira Bradley arguing with Tyrone. The whole estate had erupted into chaos and he'd given the two officers a couple of old jackets that he knew he'd never see again to escape unnoticed from the estate.

He'd never witnessed anything like it. Sharon Bradley seemed to have mobilised an army and Jackson felt something stir inside him that he hadn't experienced for a long time: pride. He heard noises outside and wondered if it was all kicking off again. He flicked on the TV: the footage was all over the news. News channels were calling it a raid. The police had been made to look like dicks. Some high-ranking bird had given a statement backing the force, yet at the same time praising the residents of the estate as heroes for helping with ongoing inquiries. What a load of horse shit.

Through the window he saw lights and figures moving around. People were coming out onto the streets again, carrying and dragging items from their homes. His eyes adjusted to the light and he realised that they were building a fucking blockade. He smiled to himself and closed the curtain, then went to the sofa and sat down, picking up the bag that the coppers had left him. Jackson had always complied in the past, to an extent, knowing the power of an institution willing to bend the rules, but these guys weren't just wanting to buckle regulations a little; they were wanting to fucking snap them in half.

He looked inside the bag. It contained everything he needed to frame a friend. When he'd asked what was in it for him, he'd been told that if he didn't do it, they could easily do the same to him. Before touching any of the contents, he pulled on a pair of gloves. Then he took out a small bag of hairs, a vial of fluid, and a box containing smudges of something between two slides. It was a veritable buffet of critical evidence.

He didn't need to ask why. Tyrone Fenton wasn't the sharpest tool in the drawer and he had a tendency to fire from the hip. There were reasons why he had a clean record, none of them to do with innocence, but that was by the by. They were trying to frame him, and it would be easy to pull it off. It had been done before.

He'd been told that if he wanted life on the estate to return to normal, he had to go ahead and do what was asked of him. If not, things would get ugly. Two pigs had been seriously hurt tonight, beaten half to death, and Jackson knew reprisals were coming. The coppers sitting in his flat had been unaware of that fact at the time; he'd seen it later, on the news. Was it better for him to be securely on the winning side? But which *was* the winning side? From where he was sitting, the cops had well and truly lost tonight's battle, but did that mean that was the end of it? Not likely.

Everyone knew that the heat being imposed on the estate wasn't some coincidental new government initiative, but a knee-jerk response to the fact that the murdered woman in Potton Park was a clean-living, well-bred, harmless, wealthy white member of this broken society of theirs. On the other hand, Keira was ill-educated, promiscuous, mixed race and poor, making her insignificant.

The police had made it clear to him that they wanted a clean and quick end to all of this so the Beacon Estate could go back to normal. By normal, Jackson assumed they meant quiet. No one was looking to improve or even save the estate; the powers-that-be just wanted them to get back into their box, and do it discreetly. Jackson surmised that for this to happen, the easiest thing would be for the same person to be guilty of both crimes, and he was sure that the evidence in the bag would prove just that. People could then go back to believing that the police were doing their job in keeping respectable citizens safe, the status quo would be restored, and the public could be told that the Beacon Estate was calm once more. There was one problem: Sharon Bradley. Jackson found himself admiring her.

A flutter settled under his ribcage. It was a familiar feeling, but one that he hadn't felt in recent years. It was the sensation of ambition. Occasionally Jackson believed that he could do something different; something that wasn't dictated by his background. Maybe a university degree, or a decent job. But then, after a minute or so, the ripple of excitement would dissipate, and he'd move on, accepting his lot and status. It was the same for everyone on the estate: the expectation to be mediocre.

The cops this afternoon had emphasised the point. He had zero prospects; in other words, he was worthless.

He had no future, no family, no meaningful relation-ships and no potential. That was what they always told him when they wanted something. But this situation was different. It occurred to him that the effort with which the two coppers had tried to coerce him was unusual. They were desperate.

But was he? He'd known of informers who'd made mistakes in the past and ended up with a knife in their guts up to their ribcage. Or who'd disappeared. He had a difficult choice to make. His actions could save the establishment and they could all go back to the unex-ceptional mainstream. Thing was, could he accept the injustice?

Sharon Bradley wasn't yielding, so why should he? He knew enough about the police to know that the murder of the middle-class woman would have rattled the senior ranks: it looked bad that it could occur in broad daylight in the middle of a park used by kids. They needed a fall guy and he'd been asked to help. Well, threatened actually. But he'd detected a sniff of panic in the coppers' tone, and he suspected they were under pressure too. It was the higher ranks who ran gigs like this: informants and snitches. They were called snouts, narks, grasses and finks. But the two coppers who'd sat in his lounge, trying to keep their shit together, were just as exploited as he was. He could tell from their eyes that they were doing somebody else's dirty work.

He needed to get to Tyrone, but without drawing attention to himself. He went to the window again and peered out. There was no sign of the police, only more and more people spilling out onto the streets, adding stuff to the makeshift blockade. Sharon was becoming a social hub for the estate: a kind of mascot championing the little people. He smiled again. He wasn't about to give in.

He felt alive.

The temperature had plummeted once more, and they were all waiting for snow, but nothing was stopping these residents who kept bringing stuff to block the road outside Wordsworth Towers. The estate looked like a grey pile of shit, while the mountains – not that he could see them from his flat – would be covered in blankets of the kind of white stuff that didn't kill you. He wished he was out there, free from any kind of manipulation and obligation.

He'd considered joining the Mountain Rescue, but then he'd also dreamt of being a lawyer. People like him didn't do decent things like that. The minute his mother shot her first bit of brown into her veins, his life was over. Not that he felt sorry for himself; on the contrary, his life was relatively good. He had friends, he enjoyed his bikes and he wanted for little. He just hadn't had any fire in his belly. But since watching the events unfold from his window, he'd begun to lift his head.

The two coppers had been very specific about what he was to do with the evidence. And now that he'd cleared his head and considered what Sharon was doing for the memory of her daughter, it gave him an idea. Maybe he could play them at their own game and use the evidence to the advantage of the whole estate?

Why face danger when you could chug along, causing no ripples on the surface of life? But this wasn't a ripple, it was a fucking tsunami. His life was about to change, and it was up to him to decide if it was to be for the better.

He looked at himself in the mirror above the electric fire in his poky living room.

He knew exactly what he would do with the contents of the bag.

Chapter 22

Tyrone Fenton relaxed on a dirty sofa, contemplating his next deal. As he listened to Lil Shane, one of the many drill-rap artists from Chicago that filled the bedrooms and lounges of ninety per cent of the flats on the estate, he repeated the lyrics without thinking about them. Analysis wasn't necessary: the songs spoke of sex, violence, knives and drugs. The usual. His lips mumbled the complicated rap lyrics, learned verbatim from hours of exposure. Lil Shane was a current favourite because he'd been arrested in the USA for drugs and murder charges. A rival had had his head blown off and Lil Shane had been at the scene. The content of his music gained the attention of the state troopers straight away, but fans knew that it was just an excuse to put another brother behind bars for fucking the system. Riots had erupted on the streets of several US cities and the President had made an unprecedented speech about closing in on the violent subculture threatening to ruin respectable society.

It was a revolution. Fuck the state.

Tyrone's body moved with the beat, and he banged the sofa, getting up to pace up and down when he grew impatient with stillness. He wore his hood up, even indoors, as if someone might spot him through the walls. The room was thick with sweet smoke and he was hungry. He went to the kitchen to see if he could find something to eat, but the TV caught his attention when he heard Keira's name.

He wiped his nose on the sleeve of his black sweater. Cocaine crystals sat inside his nostrils and he ran his finger round them and rubbed the residue on his gums. He'd been tidy. He'd done his job and taken the weapon and the clothes to a safe place until the heat died down and they could be disposed of. He still daren't go out around the estate, though; he knew the cops were looking for him. Of course they were: he'd been fucking Keira not an hour before she died. It looked bad, and he had no way out.

His thoughts turned to the girl he'd watched being butchered, helpless to do anything about it, and it hurt like hell. Problem was, he was more scared of the Cotton brothers than he was in love with Keira. That was why the drugs helped; they numbed the pain. When he was high, he didn't see her face as the blade made its first hole in her body. She'd been held like an animal and slaughtered, and there was nothing Tyrone could do about it. He wished Jackson was here. Jackson always knew what to do, and he stayed out of trouble. Tyrone could never manage that for himself.

The door banged and he heard Adam Cotton's voice. His heart sank. He rubbed his hand where deep cuts had been hastily bandaged in his flat before being told to leave by the Cotton brothers, and come here. He didn't regret trying to get the knife off Adam. Keira had seen it; she knew he wasn't part of it and that was good enough for him. But the fact that he'd run away and left her hurt him inside.

'Bruv, you look proper scared!' Adam's voice was menacing, designed to humiliate. He was flanked by syco-phants who came and went with the brothers. Of the pair, it was Adam who was more unhinged and unpre-dictable. He got up to shit that not even Jason knew about. Everyone predicted that one day he would make a mistake and get them all into trouble, and that day had arrived. The killing of the jogger was a huge mistake, though Tyrone had no idea why he'd done it. He looked beyond Adam to the door and realised that Jason wasn't with him. He wished Jackson was here even more.

'Calm down, fam, you look shit scared!' Adam laughed, obviously entertained by Tyrone's discomfort. Tyrone sweated and wished he could leave, but he had nowhere to go and the police were hunting for him. He was trapped.

He noticed that Adam had a holdall with him. He disappeared into a bedroom, re-emerging without it. Tyrone assumed that it was more incriminating evidence for him to look after until the heat died down. He wasn't in charge; all he did was follow orders and do what he was told. The flat was a safe house used for deals, deci-sions, counting money, swapping merchandise, stashing weapons and the odd whoring. It wasn't the only one: they had several dotted about the estate and the pigs had no idea where they were.

The Cotton brothers had a reputation for the best-grade gear. Most of it came from Manchester, some even as far away as London. County-lines trading had taken a sharp upturn since gangs realised that urban police were given more money for busting drugs rings than those in the provinces. They stayed one step ahead of the police

145

by trading in the least likely places: middle-class suburbs, schools, warehouses, gyms and National Trust car parks. Once the coppers got wind of a phone network, the gangs would move on, replacing the lines with new phones from different provinces. It was how the Cotton brothers had survived for so long: they were big boys in a little town, not the other way around.

Life avoiding drug squads was like guerrilla warfare in the concrete jungle. Of course some big names had gone down for serious time. Only last year a county-lines gang in Preston had been banged up for a total of eighty-two years. But for every one caught, there were thirty waiting to fill the gap. It was truly an underworld where survival depended on the network of the gang family and not the usual realms of society with their fucked-up rules and outdated methods. Ganglands had their own rhythms, their own language, their own organisations and economies, their own laws and even their own music. They should be used as models in college to teach kids how to be entrepreneurs, Jason often said, fancying himself as some kind of philosopher.

Tyrone listened as Adam talked to his hangers-on; noticed that Adam kept bringing up Sharon Bradley. He was agitated, and Tyrone wondered what Keira's mum had done to deserve such attention. He remembered Sharon through the eyes of her daughter as a sponger, a lazy old hag who nagged her constantly.

Apparently she was becoming a problem. He listened as they discussed what she'd been up to and the appearance of some kind of blockade as a protest against the police. It stoked his interest and made him change his opinion of Keira's mother. At least someone was doing something about her death. She was basically going round the estate with a loudhailer promising everlasting life to anyone coming forward for the sake of the community. Tyrone quite liked the sound of it. Unlike Adam, who wanted to get rid of her the only way he knew how. Though apparently Jason was having none of it.

The tension between the brothers had always been a point of contention. Jason was the more intelligent of the two and always gained the upper hand. Adam did as he was told. Word was they had an informer, but no one knew who it was. Tyrone remembered one squealer, three years ago, who came to the attention of the Cotton brothers after bragging about something and nothing. They found out he'd spoken to the police and figured himself immune. He'd been tortured for five hours and finally dumped, bagged and weighted, into the Duddon Estuary. No one missed him. A lot of the kids who got recruited had no family, or if they did, they were so fucked up and dysfunctional that their absence wasn't noticed or reported. Adam in particular had enjoyed ripping out the guy's fingernails, saying that it sounded like sucking pork ribs. Tyrone had laughed along with everyone else, but inside, it fuelled his worst nightmares.

More people arrived at the flat. The place was also used as a social hub for a select few. Sometimes it was where challenges were settled. A challenge could be one guy directly in beef with another, but it could also be a feud that had rumbled on for months. Jason Cotton was the one who usually decided where they were settled. It might be in a park, a warehouse, or one of these flats, if it involved high-ranking gang members.

A knife was pulled, and Tyrone heard Jason's voice.

'Fucking put that away, you twat.'

Everyone knew how hard it was to survive a direct knife fight. The two antagonists shook hands and Tyrone saw relief in their faces. Tyrone himself had never been directly challenged, and he wanted to keep it that way. Most of the violence he'd witnessed was as a result of rival gangs entering their patch, or vice versa: them travelling to patches where they weren't welcome. He'd been knifed a few times but he'd been lucky; the NHS had put a plaster on his gashes and he'd walked away.

'What you been up to, Adam?' Jason questioned his brother directly and something in the room shifted. Tyrone knew that Adam was in trouble for something, and they all assumed it was because of what had happened to the jogger in Potton Park. Word was Adam had made a mistake and slashed the wrong person. He'd had a young recruit with him and thought it clever to initiate him with a brazen attack in broad daylight.

Jason wasn't impressed, though.

'Don't know what you mean. Mother's.'

'Yes you fucking do. Don't swear on our mother's life, man. I told you to do a random, and you do a fucking posh chick in jogging gear, you fucking retard.'

Adam's face went pink and he looked away.

Tyrone knew what was coming; he'd seen Jason like this before. He wouldn't tolerate being made a fool of. He nodded to two guys, who walked up behind Adam and held his arms.

'Man! Bruv! What you doing? It was nuffin'. I swear, it wasn't me. It was someone else in your yard, fam.'

The first blow was sickening, and Adam squealed, but with the subsequent connections between knuckle and face, he grew quiet.

By the time Jason had finished, blood gushed from Adam's face and spatters covered the floor. He slumped down and everyone froze, not knowing what to expect next. Jason turned the music up and asked if anyone fancied KFC.

Chapter 23

'Hey, how you doing?' Kelly went to Josie and opened her arms. Josie fell into them and hugged her. It was funny how Josie had slowly had more and more impact on her life, and now she felt like the girl's mother. In fact, Josie visited her own mother pretty rarely, a fact the woman blamed on Johnny. But Josie was old enough to make her own mind up. Any divisions Johnny had suffered with his daughter now seemed to have been healed, and through the power of love alone. Josie was happy here.

'I'm good. I had a therapy session today.'

'How did it go?'

Johnny appeared wearing an apron, and Kelly kissed him.

'I don't really know. We just kind of sit and she plays me these meditative scripts. I feel stoned afterwards.'

'That good?'

Johnny rolled his eyes. Josie was more candid with Kelly than she was with him, and he was slightly jealous, but feigned disapproval when they discussed drugs, gangs and boys. Now, more than ever, it was important to have open discourse about the realities of teenage life, though Johnny didn't have the same skill set. He'd counselled hundreds of soldiers through PTSD but he couldn't discuss tragedy and pain with his daughter; he didn't know how to start. So he listened to Kelly do it, and it worked. Josie opened up to her.

'Have you caught them yet?' Josie asked. She was nervy as a result of the accident, and any bad news made her worse.

'No. But we will. The family are doing a press conference in the morning.'

'Wow. I can't imagine how hard that's going to be.'

'I know. The son is around your age and he's quite determined to go through with it. It's a very courageous thing to do. Did you see the estate on the news?'

'The police raids?' Johnny said. 'Jesus, I thought we were watching downtown New York!'

'President Trump tweeted that out streets are worse,' Josie said.

'You follow him on Twitter?' Johnny was surprised.

'Dad, he's hilarious. He just says it like it is, no spin, no pandering to the electorate or anything; not like our politicians. All ours want is to trick us into voting for them.'

'Can't argue with that,' Johnny said.

'What's cooking?' Kelly asked. She took off her coat. It had been a gruelling day and she couldn't shake the feeling that her job was in jeopardy. If she didn't get the results Ormond wanted, or if she offended him or made him look incompetent, she had no doubt that she would pay for it with her career. The thought terrified her, because she'd spent her whole adult life building it to where it was now. She had no idea what she'd do without it.

'Chicken curry. I'll get you a drink.'

Kelly sat down on the sofa. Johnny's place was small but tidy, and cosy with the fire lit. He and Josie had found a rhythm that suited them, and it involved her too. Sitting with Josie chatting comfortably about her work and life, with Johnny in the kitchen, felt like the most natural thing. For a fleeting moment she imagined bringing a child of her own into the equation, but she pushed the thought away rapidly.

After dinner, Josie did her homework in her room, and Kelly and Johnny sat on the sofa, with her feet on his lap. They sipped wine and the TV stayed off. During a case like this, the TV was full of fake news about the inquiry, and it wound Kelly up.

'What's up?'

She smiled. 'Work.'

'Ormond?'

She nodded. With his army background, Johnny knew how a rigid rank structure was difficult to handle. The police and the armed forces were essentially the same: they did the government's dirty work. Ostensibly, government was designed to protect the people, but it did the opposite: it safeguarded the establishment in rank order. If soldiers fucked up, they went down. If generals fucked up, they were paid to keep quiet. Same was true in the police. The top brass were untouchable, even from the inside.

Reports were coming in of barricades on the Beacon Estate and Kelly was waiting to see how Ormond would tackle it. It was his doing after all. Maybe it would work to her advantage, because Sharon Bradley seemed to have been recruiting loyal followers all day. Someone, some-where, knew something. Johnny agreed.

Now that Ormond had screwed up so royally with Op Turkey, as it had become known, she hoped that he might be inclined to let her get on with the investigation.

As long as he interfered and went behind her back, she couldn't do her job properly. The problem was that he was her boss. Should she want to make a complaint, she'd have to make it independent and bring in another force, because of his rank. She knew people in the Met, obviously, but she also knew officers in Manchester who could recommend a solid chief constable. It would have to be somebody at least two ranks above Ormond, who didn't know him.

'Is it that bad?' Johnny asked, after she filled him in on her day from hell. It wasn't that Johnny didn't disbelieve her; he was just testing whether her case was watertight.

'No. That's me playing it forward. I want to be prepared if I have to go against him.'

'What's driving this?'

'The husband?' she suggested. 'They play golf together; it's all pretty cosy.'

'Surely you guys have rules on that: isn't it a conflict of interest? He shouldn't be on the investigation of the murder of a friend's wife.'

'You're right, but he kind of threatened me today, and you know rank is everything, even in today's politically correct force.' She paused. 'Me going up against a superintendent is like you, as a major, going up against a general, with all those years of experience and status. Can you imagine?'

'Yes, I can. It would never happen.'

'Without some form of backlash at least.'

He agreed.

'There's something else that doesn't sit well. Will is hiding something.' She gave him a précis of her conversation with her trusted officer and told Johnny about Liam Brook. 'Will's scared of Ormond and I don't know why.'

'Authority?'

'No, it's more than that. It's as if Ormond controls them. Something happened before I got here.'

'What?'

'I don't know.'

'You need to find out.'

'I know. Ormond's agenda is different to mine. My objective is cracking the case. His seems to be vengeance.'

'He's nearing retirement and wants to go out in a blaze of glory?'

'It's not even that. I don't get the impression he wants glory: Op Eagle was a secret.'

'So he wants to upstage you?'

'No, I think I annoy him, but not because I'm a threat. It's as if me cracking the case properly isn't part of his plan.'

'He's rushing? And therefore likely to make mistakes.'

'He's acting like a rookie.'

'What ulterior motives are possible?'

'Well, he's not losing his marbles, as he seems pretty switched on. The way he looked at me when I suggested that perhaps he needed to trust the detective work to me: it was as if he wanted me out of the way because he's hiding something possibly illegal. I've never felt that from a colleague before. Apart from my last case in London.'

'You've got to report it.'

'Who to? One of his mates at HQ? Or take your pick of sixty-year-old white males he plays golf with.'

'So, if Ormond has an illegal motive, what might that be?'

'Hmm, illegal gain out of skewing a major murder investigation...' She thought aloud. 'Money, a cover-up, or he's bent.'

'What would he be covering up?'

'Previous, as in something that the case has flagged up; or current, as in the fact that he's promised Thomas Watson he'll get answers. Emotions: they fuck most things up.'

'What other cases does this possibly link to?'

'Drugs?'

'Your gut?' he asked.

'When I was in London, the coppers I saw busted for being bent, and on the take, were the ones no one suspected. But I'm on shaky ground here. I need to look into it. It's unusual behaviour for a senior officer with so much experience. I need to dig into his past, and see what motivates him.'

'Another investigation to add to your list?'

'I know, it sounds crazy. But he knows that I'm unhappy, and I'm annoyed with myself for letting on.'

'You couldn't help it: it was your natural response to him being a muppet.'

'Exactly. The look on his face when I confronted him: I saw it in his eyes. He knows I know, and I reckon he's going to try to get rid of me. He's never waded into one of my investigations before, apart from to authorise Armed Response or get a last-minute warrant. Never. And him being pals with Thomas Watson isn't enough in my mind to take such risks.'

Johnny stroked her arm. They didn't need to speak any more. Tonight, she could switch off and allow herself to be taken care of. Tomorrow she'd dig into Ormond and look a little closer at Will and Liam's career paths. For the first time since she'd left London, she was fearful for her reputation and her job. She was used to searching for bastards, but not in her own back yard.

Chapter 24

On Friday morning, Thomas Watson and his two children arrived at Eden House for a press conference. When they entered the building, the place fell silent and they were greeted by a sea of sympathetic faces. From uniforms on the front desk to civilian workers sitting at computers, the caretakers emptying waste bins and, through the back, into the room that was used for press conferences such as this, the detectives setting up the tables: everyone felt their pain.

All coppers knew what grief did to a human face: it sank it deep within itself, leaving cavernous shadows etched around the eyes through lack of sleep. Rest was a thing of the past for this family: they spent their waking moments – when not collapsed for an hour here and there through sheer exhaustion – running their reality through the cogs of their inner brains, trying to figure out why... why... why. On and on it whirred, relentless. If only Mum had decided to run along the lake that day instead, if only Millie had been off school ill and she'd stayed home to care for her, if only Thomas had decided to open a bottle of Argentinian Malbec from the cellar the night before and she'd decided to skip her run with a hangover. If only.

Getting out of the house, away from the home created by the woman they all loved, had brought a slight diversion to the threesome; they could distract their minds with stuff not of her making: street lamps, dogs being walked, the sky, traffic lights, the noise of cars and so forth. Within the walls of Eden House, however, the enormity of their loss confronted them once more, violently and shamelessly. Millie held onto her father's arm; Jordan walked solemnly behind, not daring to make eye contact lest he should crumble into a sobbing mess in front of all of these police officers.

It was bad enough that they had to face the press. But they all agreed they had no choice. Of course it had to be done. Dad had decided to offer a cash reward too. Some cowardly bastards out there knew something, and money made people talk. Dad had explained that the police officer in charge was a woman called Kelly Porter and that she was nice. Jordan asked what had happened to the man called Neil who'd visited the house, and he'd been told that Neil was far more senior than a mere detective and was overseeing the whole investigation. They knew about the other murder the following morning, but they hadn't been told if the two were connected. Jordan felt slightly better that a high-ranking police officer was involved.

They were shown into a large room that was like a school classroom. A woman and a man waited for them, and they watched their dad greet the woman called Kelly. The man was called Will. Jordan couldn't bear the looks they gave him – it was something that he'd soon realised was set on everyone's face now: sympathy. He hated it.

There were some papers laid out on the table and Kelly asked if she could go through them: there were photos of their mum, she explained, and she wanted them to be ready. The three of them had chosen them the previous day. One depicted their mother in running kit, laughing; another showed just her beautiful face, staring into the camera. They'd also picked out one of the whole family because it had been tactfully mentioned that the more emotive the photos, the more profound the public response. The more TV viewers were faced with the true human impact of crime, the more likely they were to pick up the phone or email in.

Kelly turned over the photos and Millie let out a gasp and grabbed her dad.

'Let's sit down,' Kelly said. Jordan liked her. She was strong, he could tell. It was something in her eyes that made him feel as though she had their backs. She was a bit like his mum, and he imagined her being stern but fair with her kids. He wagered that she was a good mum, like his. Millie whimpered, and Dad cradled her.

'Millie, you don't have to do this,' Jordan said to his sister.

'Dad, I can't...' she said. Her voice was tortured, and Jordan's fists clenched open and shut. His anger was like a white-hot metal cable pulsing through every blood vessel in his body, charging him with the strength he needed to get through today for Millie and Dad, but also to focus on whatever he needed to do to get revenge. He knew a few guys at school who had links with the Beacon Estate. He had names. He could easily work out addresses. He'd even contemplated setting up fake drug deals, to get inside the crew. He had all the time in the world. Mum wasn't coming back; there was no deadline. He had no other ambition than to find the two men who'd killed her and spend time alone with them. He knew how easy it was to work one's way into a gang; Christ, they groomed volunteers for a living. He could easily, in the midst of his agonising grief, turn to drugs and misdeeds. Once on the slippery slope, he'd grow hard and dangerous, trusted by the inner few. The thought thrilled him.

'If Millie would like to sit out, I can stay with her, Thomas,' Kelly said.

'I'm sorry, Dad,' Millie whispered. Thomas held her and soothed her, then looked at Jordan.

'It's me and you, son,' he said.

Jordan took his father's outstretched hand and shook it, nodding his allegiance. He saw Kelly glance at him and he read her face: she was impressed with him and he knew he could go through with it. He'd begun burying his feelings the moment he'd been given the news. Now, he could burn himself on the kettle or pull a muscle in their home gym lifting ludicrously heavy weights and not feel it until after. There was a reason: he had a purpose.

'There are around twenty journalists waiting in the next room,' Kelly said. 'I'm going to brief them, then I'll take Millie away through that door and the press will file in. When you're ready, you can read your prepared statement. Will is in charge; he'll guide you through and make sure everybody knows you're not taking questions at this time. That's still your decision?'

Thomas looked at Jordan and they both nodded agreement. It had been Thomas's decision. They wanted to get the attention of the public, especially those living on the Beacon Estate, and they agreed that a powerful appeal was all that was required. The public would have their own questions and would ponder them, rather than turn it into a circus. The news about the trouble on the estate last night was making headlines and the residents must be getting sick and tired of the negative attention; this might be their opportunity to raise awareness of the conditions in which they lived. Jordan wasn't stupid. He knew he was privileged. He knew how money dictated your path in life, more than any other single factor. His father was a wealthy man; that was why he was offering £100,000 in cash for information leading to any arrests.

Dad's friend Neil had told them that their mum's murder had become national news because of the brazen nature of the attack, and the fact that no one was safe any more. Random knife violence was no longer the preserve of gangs in inner cities; it had spilled into the suburbs and a middle-class mother of two was dead. The arbitrary nature of the crime had chilled middle England and, sadly, Keira Bradley's murder had become a sideline. Jordan didn't much care about the details of the other woman who'd been stabbed to death; his mind was on one thing only. She did have a use, though. Jordan had already suggested to his father that he arrange to meet Sharon Bradley. He'd followed the news on TV and watched as Sharon Bradley mobilised hundreds of people. It was inspiring and Jordan had felt something stir inside him: Sharon Bradley was *doing* something. He'd watched the footage of the barricades being constructed, and the desire of people from all over to join in.

Kelly told them that there were journalists from all over the country and a few from Europe. Mum's death was being used as an example of the precarious level of security on Britain's streets. That was fine by him; they could do what they liked as long as it was kept in the news. He stared at his favourite picture of his mother: the one of her in her running kit. He'd taken it with his iPhone. She'd been going for a run along the lake and had forgotten her headphones. He and Millie had been getting ready for school and she'd shouted from the kitchen, asking if somebody could get them from upstairs so she didn't have to take her trainers off. Jordan had run downstairs wearing just a towel and she'd laughed. He couldn't remember what had prompted him to snap her with his phone, apart from that it irritated her. She hated having her photo taken.

'Delete it!' she'd hollered as she left. He was eternally grateful that he hadn't.

'Ready?' Kelly asked.

A flustered police officer in a fancy uniform rushed in, and Jordan recognised him as Dad's friend Neil. He went straight to Dad and took his hand.

'Superintendent,' DI Porter said. Jordan looked at the DI and then at Neil: he was obviously her boss, and he reckoned they didn't like one another.

Neil coughed, and Dad nodded.

'I'm just about to brief the press, sir,' DI Porter said.

Neil nodded. 'I'll take a back seat, Tom,' he said. As he walked to a chair behind the table, he patted Jordan on his shoulder and smiled that pained smile at him. Jordan decided that he didn't like him either; he felt sorry for Kelly having to work for him.

The other officer, Will, brought their attention back to why they were here, and gave some last-minute instructions to do with timings and when he would use the images. It was a blur.

Kelly left the room and Jordan heard the buzz of anticipation from the journalists. He'd never been to a press conference, though he'd seen plenty of them during his A-level media lessons. He couldn't imagine himself sitting his A levels now. He'd likely be in prison by then for murder.

Kelly came back and held her hand out to Millie, who took it. She turned to Dad.

'There are a few more than we thought. Are you ready?'

He nodded.

Once Kelly and Millie had left, Neil took a seat behind the table and Thomas and Jordan joined him. Will checked one last time that they were ready, then went to the door and opened it. Dozens of people flooded in and took seats, but strangely, there was little noise. Jordan saw it again: sympathy. It galvanised him and gave him the strength to do what he had to do. When the noise of bodies and equipment moving had stopped, and only the clicking of cameras and the shuffling of papers remained, Will began.

Jordan reflected on all the speeches he'd given at school: for debating club, English language exams and history role plays. He'd never imagined in all that time that he'd one day be sitting next to a police officer, analysing the power of speech. He listened intently and graded Will on his powers of communication, and he was pleasantly surprised. The officer showed intelligence and flair, despite the tough task before him. He was a typical copper: to the point, monotone and brief, but he had passion. He spoke with genuine attention to detail. Then it was Dad's turn. Jordan held his hand and the cameras clicked. It created a cacophony of mechanical tumult that hurt his head. He tried to concentrate. He'd written his father's speech. No one coughed, fidgeted or fiddled. Jordan loved his father more in that moment than ever, and even contemplated abandoning his plan because he knew how much he'd let him down should he go through with it. But something was wrong. Dad had frozen. Jordan looked at him and at Will, then he faced the cameras. Will held up photos of Ella. Jordan didn't need notes.

'My mother was brutally attacked and murdered for no reason.'

The cameras clicked and flashed. No one else said a word. Thomas covered his face.

'She wasn't hated, or in trouble. She'd done nothing wrong.'

He paused and took a deep breath. His throat grew tight and his eyes stung, but he was determined to finish.

'Her absence is something that we have to live with forever, but those who did this will only face the consequences if they are caught. And they will only be caught with your help.' He stared at every camera that he could see, in turn. 'I am begging anyone who knows anything about this crime to call the police – anonymously if you prefer – to help us catch these people, so that we can reach some kind of peace, but most importantly to make sure they are never able to do this again. We would like to share our sympathy with the family of Keira Bradley.'

Neil shifted in his seat. A rumble of questions stirred the room.

'My father is offering one hundred thousand pounds for any information that leads to a conviction for the murder of my mother. We are begging the local community to come together and realise that we're all the same. The death of Keira Bradley must take the same priority as my mother's, and my father is offering the same amount for information leading to a conviction for that too.'

The press went wild. Jordan locked eyes with Will and saw admiration, but when he glanced at Neil, it was the very opposite; it was almost distaste. He made a note to discuss it with his father.

'The family is not taking questions at this time,' Will announced. 'Thank you all for coming.'

They were escorted out of the room and Jordan went to sit with Millie and the detective. He overheard Neil speaking to his father.

'You don't have to go through with it; it can be explained as a knee-jerk reaction and can be retracted.'

Jordan realised that he was talking about his father offering a reward for information about Keira's death.

Chapter 25

After the press conference, Neil Ormond made rapid excuses to leave and headed back to HQ, where he scanned the initial report on Op Eagle. It made for uncomfortable reading, but the officer responsible had papered over the more serious flaws, and he was satisfied. No one could have predicted the sheer size and mood of the crowds on the Beacon Estate. All procedure had been followed and arrests had been made. There were dozens of interviews being conducted across the Penrith area today, all contributing to the inquiry into the murder of Ella Watson, and that of Keira Bradley, of course. Though what Thomas Watson was thinking wasting his money on that was anyone's guess.

At sixty, Ormond was nearing retirement, and his wife thought he'd spent too much time on the force as it was. He'd been offered a decent payout three years ago, but couldn't give up the habit. His wife had virtually begged him to take the money and leave. She dreamed of spending the rest of their days on a cruise ship; he couldn't think of anything worse. She'd felt bitterly let down when he'd told her that the constabulary needed him to stay on. It was a lie, but she eventually accepted it. The thing was, he couldn't begin to imagine what civilian life would be like, without power and influence. He'd lived and breathed the uniform for almost forty years. A retirement plan was in place, but there were a few loose ends to tie up before he could bear to let go. The murder of Ella Watson was one of them.

Thomas was a shadow of his former self. Ormond had watched as the man morphed into a two-dimensional caricature, his voice monosyllabic and his eyes dead. He'd seen enough victims of crime to know that the early days were life-changing, but you had to keep going. The boy, Jordan, had done a sterling job at the press conference, though offering a hundred thousand pounds for information on the Bradley case was ludicrous. He'd told him so, but Tom wouldn't budge.

The murder of the street girl was something they saw all the time, and even expected. It wasn't that he didn't care; it was that Ella's death was the more shocking because she was a decent woman, minding her own business, killed for a random bet: or that was how he understood initiation rites. He'd done his homework and DI Porter had confirmed it in so many words. Gangs all over the world initiated new members in similar ways and, recently, stabbings of strangers were on the increase. However, he now had to accept that there was no evidence yet that the killings were linked. His original plan had been derailed.

It made him sick to his stomach. And DI Porter was not doing enough. How dare she question him on such matters? Her ridiculous adherence to the churning of evidence was slowing them down. Of course it was necessary, but HOLMES was perfectly capable of keeping the case up to date. Human resources were better placed doing what a computer couldn't: thinking. Ella had been murdered on Wednesday, and it was Friday already.

Porter had instinct. He knew that. But he got the feeling that she was going to present problems. He wanted to follow the case in a certain way, and yesterday had displayed her lack of imagination perfectly. She'd turned up at his office, read him an abridged version of the riot act and acted like a premenstrual teenager; he should know, he'd raised two.

He'd already looked into the promotion of young Will Phillips to DI, a move that would make DI Porter's presence peripheral. Then she could be moved to a desk job somewhere to keep her quiet. But Phillips was still young; he needed a hero moment to make him stand out. Through his ex-colleague, Liam Brook, he also had strong ties to the community policing on the Beacon Estate. Some bonds, formed in youth, couldn't be broken. Ormond was also considering secondment for Porter. She'd done a successful stint in London earlier in the year: he could send her back there, or even abroad. The EU was always asking for international representation on legal teams across the Continent. Even after Brexit, Interpol would always need the experience of good officers who'd proved their mettle. And he couldn't deny that Porter had shown her worth.

He glanced at his computer screen. A police computer was the most robustly protected service available, and he took full advantage of that by handling all of his business affairs through it. No one was allowed in his office unless invited; it was a haven in which he could operate in complete privacy. There would always be too many questions at home. Here, he could create dozens of passwords and elevate confidentiality simply by encrypting each file for his eyes only. He'd been doing it for years.

He looked at the screen and checked the balance of his offshore account in the Isle of Man. The government was tightening the noose around such tax loopholes and so he was in the process of transferring the whole lot into a new business venture here on the mainland. But it was tedious work and he left his accountant to sort out the detail.

He picked up his mobile and dialled a number.

'Ormond here,' he bellowed when the call was answered. He nodded and exchanged pleasantries, then dropped his voice, never sure of who might be listening.

'I need some information on a fellow officer, and I need the utmost discretion,' he said. 'I want you to find something I can use. And while you're at it, find out what she values the most in her life: cat, car, children… you get the idea.'

There was a short pause.

'Her name is Detective Inspector Kelly Porter.'

He hung up and punched a different number into his phone.

'Has it been done?'

'Yes, guv.'

He was the gaffer and no one else.

Chapter 26

'How well do you know Neil, Dad?'

Thomas Watson was driving his children home. Millie was quiet in the back, and Jordan sat up front with his father.

'Just from the golf club. He was one of the first people to reach out to us when we moved here.' The memory pained him and he bit his lip. Jordan saw it and stared out of the window.

'I don't like him.'

'Why ever not? He's a thoroughly decent man.'

'He might be decent on the outside, but his staff don't like him, and he looked disgusted when I said you were offering a reward for information about Keira's death.'

'I agree, Dad,' Millie piped up. 'I don't think Kelly likes him either. She's sharp around him.'

'Maybe he's acting strangely because he doesn't know what else to do. I mean, he knew your mother personally. He has the resources and the power to make this investigation a priority. It can't be easy being that close and not getting answers.'

'It's only been two days!' Jordan's outburst was aggressive and his father admonished him. All their nerves were frayed and it was becoming increasingly wearing living under the same roof as one another. Only Grandma kept them from snapping all the time.

'Are you going to call Sharon Bradley?'

Thomas shifted in his seat. 'I don't think she'll want to talk to me. I'm a complete stranger. She's obviously super busy anyway.'

'You're avoiding the issue, Dad. You've just offered a hundred K for finding out who killed her daughter!' It was Jordan's turn to scold his father. 'You think she'll be too busy? I think you're scared.'

'What?'

Millie listened intently to the exchange.

'You don't want to get your hands dirty. You see Keira and her family as beneath us. You're too cowardly to reach out because you think they're not the same.'

His father gripped the wheel and Millie sank lower in her seat.

'How dare you!'

'It's true, Dad. Drop me off here, I want to walk.'

'No!'

'Dad, I'm sixteen. Stop the car or I'll give up my A levels.' Jordan's voice was even and calm.

'What? This is hardly the time to make empty threats, Jordan, I'm warning you!'

'Warning me of what? You have no power over me. You don't even know what I like to eat. You have no idea what my favourite chocolate is. You don't know if I'm gay or straight. Mum knew all of those things. Stop the fucking car!'

Thomas did as he was asked. His hands shook on the steering wheel and he swallowed hard as his son got out of the car, slamming the door with all his might. They were in Pooley Bridge. Millie opened her door and shouted after her brother, but he ignored her. She got in the front passenger seat and shut the door.

'He needs time, Dad. Come on, let's go home.'

Thomas watched as his son turned off the main road, and tears ran down his face.

'Dad?'

He turned to her. 'I'm sorry.'

–

Once the car was out of sight, Jordan went back to the main road and walked aimlessly back in the direction of Penrith. It was freezing, and snow fell lightly. Up on the hills, it was like a thick blanket, but on the roads it settled then turned to mush. They were due a big dump soon. He fastened his coat against the wind and kept his head down. A car slowed and a man poked his head through the open window.

'You all right, mate? Need a lift?'

'You going to Penrith?' Jordan asked.

'Yep, can I drop you there?'

'Please, thank you.' Jordan got into the passenger seat and the man set off.

'What you doing walking all that way? You had an argument with your folks?' The man stared at him. 'You were on TV this morning! The appeal?'

'Yes, that's me.' Jordan didn't change his facial expression; it remained mute and emotionless. He didn't know what he felt or thought any more.

'I'm sorry about your mother,' the stranger said. Jordan stared straight ahead. 'I guess you've had enough of all that bollocks, eh?'

Jordan looked at him and nodded.

'So how come you're in the middle of nowhere? Where's your dad?'

'I got out of the car.'

'Argument?'

'Everything's different now.'

'That's a lot of money to be offering. I guess your old fella has a few quid?'

'We're all right.'

'You know people on the Beacon Estate don't talk. I don't think he'll have to put his hand in his pocket any time soon.'

'You reckon? Not for two hundred grand?' Jordan asked.

'They're a tight lot. I used to live there myself.'

'How did you...'

'Escape?' The man laughed. 'It's all right, I'm not offended. I studied hard at school. Got a good job. It's the only way. I bet you don't go to school in Penrith, do you?'

'No, Keswick.'

'Dad pay?'

Jordan nodded. 'I hate it now.'

'Figures. It won't last forever. You're angry.'

Jordan stared out of the window, trying to figure out how he came to be in this man's car talking about his feelings. Some people were good after all.

'Where you going?'

'The Beacon Estate.'

'What for?'

Jordan didn't answer.

'Revenge?'

'Maybe.'

'Not worth it, kid. They'll be caught, you'll see.'

Jordan stared at him. 'Why do you have all this... belief? This hope?'

'What else is there?'

They carried on in silence to the centre of Penrith. The man wished him luck when he dropped him off. It felt odd. Jordan walked around and around aimlessly, undecided what to do, only sure of the fact that he didn't want to go home. He felt foolish and decided against going to the Beacon Estate. He'd ignored ten calls from Millie and felt bad about it.

He told her he'd get a bus to Pooley Bridge and walk from there. She said she needed to get out of the house too and wanted to meet him.

Chapter 27

The press conference had gone well, but being in such close proximity to Ormond had been a challenge for Kelly. Something in the atmosphere at Eden House had shifted. This was her patch: her manor. But it didn't feel right, and she found herself eyeing everyone suspiciously, even her team.

She'd said very little to Will before he accompanied her to the press room to ready the Watson family. They had been incredible. Jordan was a formidable young man and she felt his agony. She also saw that he hated being treated like a victim: he wanted answers and she intended to make every effort to get them. Millie was sweet and very like Josie. They were both teenagers in need of space, a voice and someone to pick up the pieces. Josie had found that with her father and with Kelly. Millie had had her support ripped away when it was most important. Away from the press, Kelly had chatted to her, and Millie had opened up about her father. She gave the impression that he wasn't coping nearly as well as he was letting on. Kelly reassured her that it was normal. She'd given Millie her personal mobile number.

Back in the incident room, the investigation ran along and no one would ever guess that Kelly was questioning the loyalty of those surrounding her. They all acknowledged her and gave her updates on what they were working on. This was usually the stage where things got busy and information began to produce results that all had to be chased. The first forty-eight hours were crucial for gathering evidence, but the processing took time and patience. She set a briefing meeting for later and went to her office.

The handling of the fallout of Op Eagle was not her concern. She'd read the transcripts of the interviews with people who'd been arrested for various offences during the raids. None of them were pertinent to her own investigation. Seven of them were still in custody, but their twenty-four-hour window without charges was dwindling, and most of them had replied 'no comment' to every question put to them, as was their right. The local solicitors had had a field day counting the fees that legal aid would provide. The innocent had to be proven guilty by the police, and if they weren't, then they were free to go. Instinct didn't count, and being in the wrong place at the wrong time didn't prove guilt by association. It was a shotgun operation and they'd lost the advantage. Maybe Ormond was in the first stages of dementia after all.

To distract herself, she sat at her desk and opened the log of what had been sent to the lab from both murder cases, sighing when she saw the sheer number of reference codes. She decided to throw herself into some work before she briefed the team, as she did every day when working a serious crime.

Lab results could take an age to return and provide them with the scraps of critical evidence needed to pass the threshold for charging. The Crime Prosecution Service had to be convinced of a conviction, otherwise it was a waste of time and taxpayers' money. Kelly had seen the sharp downturn over the last ten years in CPS willingness to approve charges being brought. It was frustrating, but the evidence had to be bombproof. She also knew what happened when the police, convinced of a person's guilt because of circumstances, fabricated a case and contrived the story. It didn't take much tampering with witness statements or timings for a person to look guilty. It happened all the time.

But now, thanks to Op Turkey, they'd lost any hope of momentum and looked like bullies. It could possibly weaken their case should they ever put one together.

Next, she watched the CCTV footage of the trouble that had erupted on the Beacon Estate. She hoped she might catch a glimpse of what Will Phillips and Liam Brook had been up to. There were two cameras: one overlooked the road adjacent to Wordsworth Towers, which seemed to be the hub of the activity; the other monitored the play area where the two officers had been cornered. The footage made her shiver. It was every officer's worst nightmare: getting trapped by an angry mob. Even with enhancing, the images were grainy when enlarged and the crowd appeared as some great heaving mass of black and dark grey. Many of the young men covered their faces with bandannas and their heads with hoods, making it almost impossible to spot indicators that could potentially identify them. Before this, Kelly had been making sense of the main players; now, there were scores of people involved. Instead of helping his friend find answers, Ormond had made it worse.

As suddenly as the mob appeared on screen, it dispersed again, though police could be seen catching several and making arrests. Then the armed-response unit arrived, and as the crowd dispersed, Kelly could see the two officers on the floor. She wondered if Ormond had seen the footage.

She called the hospital, and was told that the two men were stable. The press had been trying to gain access to the ward where they were being treated, but uniforms were guarding the entrances and only those passed by security came and went. A journalist posing as a close family member had been caught only because a bright officer had checked in with a relative he knew was in the family room. It was a close shave.

Op Turkey had attracted a wave of interest nationwide, with many headlines referring to Enoch Powell's 'Rivers of Blood' speech from 1968 warning that Britain in a mere couple of generations would be facing a bloodbath on her streets. The incendiary language was fucking unhelpful, but it had been brought upon them by a senior officer. The vast majority of streets in Britain were safe. Ormond had authorised an increased police presence on the estate, and Kelly had no choice but to allow him to wade in. All she could do was separate her inquiries from those of general law and order, and leave him to it. He'd already warned her to keep her nose clean. But she did call Sharon Bradley to assure her that the police presence was not sinister. After a tirade of abuse, involving Kelly apologising a lot, Sharon calmed down and told her what the residents had seen yesterday, including the fact that two officers had knocked on the door of Jackson Akers and gone inside. Kelly quizzed her about the young man, who Sharon seemed to have a soft spot for.

After that, she logged on to the police database and entered Neil Ormond's details. His career profile popped up and she went through it carefully. The radio crackled in the background and she heard running commentary from the estate. The unrest had rumbled on and several more barricades had popped up, with a number of females refusing to move until police gave guarantees of safety. People had brought food and drink to the makeshift barriers, and they'd became quasi camps. So far the mood was amicable. But that wasn't Kelly's concern: that was for the realm of tactical force and public order. Hopefully it'd keep Ormond occupied and off her back. And it if worked, then a collaborative Beacon Estate could only be good for her inquiries.

Ormond had begun his career almost forty years ago, in Birmingham in 1979. He'd been a bobby for seven years with no significant issues to note. In 1986 he'd transferred to Glasgow and been promoted quickly. By 1995, he was a chief inspector, and he moved to Penrith in 2000. It was a distinguished service history and there were links to various medals and awards he'd won. She clicked on some of them, hoping to find something more. The local press tended to turn up at various public events supported by the police to fill their column space. She rifled through various charity occasions and studied the faces of the philanthropists smiling into the camera. Ormond was there to shake the hands of several of them. He was quite handsome in his younger years, she noted: tall and commanding, with piercing eyes.

And then her blood froze.

She looked at the date on the photo on the screen: 2013. It showed two local businessmen flanking Ormond.

They were all holding a cheque for the better part of half a million quid, made payable to a children's home. She read the accompanying article in detail. She knew the names well. One of the men had died in prison, banged up while seriously ill with cancer, guilty of smuggling, supplying children for the purposes of sexual services, and money laundering. The other had died before he faced charges, in a poky hotel room in Ambleside, straddled by a prostitute, in control of a multimillion-pound laundering racket that supplied women, weapons and drugs to the whole of the UK. They were both predators, exploiting anything with value – mainly sex and drugs – for personal gain.

Kelly should know: she'd been the one who'd exposed them. Ormond was the superintendent when she'd investigated the case. She clicked on a link below the article.

Charity gala raises £200,000 for underprivileged children.

Another photo. The date was 2012. This time Ormond had his arms around the pair, and was laughing at some no-doubt hilarious joke told by one of them. She stared into their faces.

A quick check of the children's home and the charity that benefited from the alleged funds revealed that were both registered in Workington, and it didn't take Kelly long to make further inquiries into who owned or ran the institutions. On the board of directors was another name she recognised, and this time the hairs on her arms stood on end.

The Tombday case had unveiled a Europe-wide trafficking and money-laundering racket run by Colin Day and Barry Crawley, the two men who'd posed with

Ormond almost a decade ago, smiling, embracing and parading as chums. Back then, they'd have been at the height of their influence over vulnerable groups of people here and abroad. The question was: how much did Ormond know?

Chapter 28

Jackson was working on a Carrera Vanquish. All the kids had them, no matter their income. If it couldn't be bought, it could be nicked. It didn't take long to change seats, handlebars and spoke covers to make over a hot bike so it looked brand new. He never asked questions. Morality didn't pay. All that mattered was survival. He listened to music in the garage, and worked alone.

He was gradually creating his own gym in there, and one of his many plans was to train local kids to keep them out of trouble. He'd managed to clear a space big enough for two boxing bags and a climbing rope. He made barbells and dumb-bells out of old axles donated to him by mechanics who knew he used junk, weighting them with sand or concrete.

He heard a noise behind him and turned round, away from his bike rack. The Cotton brothers stood inside his garage, flanked by several followers. Jackson knew them all. They were a mixture of races, sexes, violent proclivities, and status. Mostly addicts and dealers. He looked at the younger ones and felt helpless to steer them away from what was inevitable. They took seats dotted around the garage and Jackson waited to see what they wanted. It wasn't a social call, and he reckoned they didn't want a bike fixing.

Maybe they wanted their gear back. The package that Tyrone had given him had come from Jason Cotton. That much he knew. Over the years, he'd been given all sorts of items to dispose of, but in reality, he kept everything. More than that, he'd kept a record of every one of them: where it was exchanged, the time, date and description of the package. The bag given to him by Tyrone contained bloody clothes and a knife. It was small enough to peel vegetables, but big enough to kill. It was clean, but Jackson knew that evidence stuck to blades like rabbit shit to fur. He also knew that it was, in all probability, the weapon that had killed Keira.

'What happened to your face, Adam?' he asked. He assumed he'd been in a dispute, and lost.

'He needed teaching a lesson, fam.' Jason clarified the situation and Jackson pieced together what had happened. Adam had gone out on a limb, taking a new member's initiation into his own hands, and his brother was pissed. But it was curious. Why would Jason give two fucks about his brother killing someone?

Jackson looked at Adam, who had his hands in his pockets and wore a hood that masked most of his wounds. It was standard attire. Two females fawned over him. The Cotton brothers were of different ethnic descent from one another, but no one ever mentioned the fact that their mother was a junkie who shagged around. Adam was black, Jason was white. What mattered was power, not creed.

Jason folded his arms. He was taller than his brother and had the brains. Adam was slimmer, but a mean mother-fucker. He stood just behind Jason. Jackson was impressed by the damage Jason had caused: he was a mean bastard too. He guessed Adam must be in a lot of pain. What a refreshing change.

''Sup, bruv?' he asked Jason directly. He played the game, and adjusted his tone and word choice for his audience.

'You been visited by two pigs, innit.' Jason leaned forward as if to intimidate Jackson. The only thing that intimidated him was the number of arseholes in front of him, not any of them individually. He sized them up. There were five males in total. Each one he'd personally witnessed visit grievous harm on young lads on the estate. Each had passed the threshold for the type of violence requiring zero empathy for the victim. There was no doubt about what they carried under their hoodies. These guys were always tooled up. There was also no doubt in his mind that one of the young men standing in his garage had been Adam Cotton's protégé on Wednesday morning in Potton Park. Most of them looked as though they were stoned, except Jason, who was switched on, as usual. That was a worry. They were evenly matched physically, but he'd never known Jason go into a fight on his own; he always had accomplices and weapons.

If they were tooled with intent, then Jackson stood no chance and had to plan an exit fast.

'So what? I said nuffin'. You know they use me like they use you, it's no different. They're bent, bruv, and worried about the killin' of the rich woman in the park. She was important.'

Jason looked at his brother, who bit his lip and walked away, sitting down heavily and lighting a pre-rolled zoot. There was a coolness between them, and Jackson noticed that, whoever this woman was, her death was a problem.

He'd seen one of the officers on TV this morning, sitting with the family of the murdered woman. Maybe the heat was as a result of the woman being respectable and not from the estate. It was a random attack, all right, but the wrong one. Adam Cotton was in trouble and he knew it. But what did they want with Jackson?

'How do we know you're not lyin', fam?'

'You known me long enough, Jason. I'm telling the truth.'

'What you do with what we gave you?' Adam asked.

The girls grew bored and one sauntered over to a sofa and promptly fell asleep.

'I did what you said, like I always do. Why would I do anything else? I'm not stupid!'

'He's fucking lying, Jason!' Adam was a loose cannon.

'Shut the fuck up, Adam, you ain't got nuffin' to say.'

Adam slunk back and shut up, glaring at Jackson, obviously desperate to find a way back into to his brother's trust. One way would be to divert interest from himself to Jackson.

'You've got a short memory, Adam,' said Jackson. 'Like when I saved your pussy at least the last three times you were knifed. Barrow? Lancaster? Glasgow?'

Jason nodded and laughed at his brother. 'He's got a point, fam. Come on, let's smoke sometin'.' He spoke like a Caribbean Rasta star; it was the language of the street. They all did it, even Jackson. Even though he didn't have black skin and he wasn't from Jamaica. He had no idea where or when he'd begun to talk like that: it was around age ten, he guessed. He just did it because everyone did. They all looked up to the years above them in school and the vocab developed from there. It drove the teachers nuts, and they kept correcting their linguistic mistakes, to no avail.

'Turn that music up,' Jason ordered.

Jackson did so and went back to the bike he was working on. His palms were sweaty and his hands shook. He swallowed hard and turned the bike slightly so he had them all in his peripheral vision. He didn't want to be caught off guard. For now, there was nothing more he could do. He'd defused a situation and he had to roll with it. He had to stay sober and alert.

Two of the men began undressing the sleeping girl and she stirred. They didn't stop. Jackson went to the fridge in the corner for beers and tried to drown out the noises coming from the girl as she was toyed with by the two men. It was commonplace. Sometimes the girls resisted, sometimes they didn't. This time, she wasn't interested in sex, but that was of no concern to the two men on top of her. A third helped hold her. The other girls goaded them on, nervous shock spilling over into bravado. But all of them moved in slow motion, fried by drugs. Even their language was dopey.

It didn't take long for Adam to lie down with two of the girls, stoned, and fall asleep. The girl who'd been degraded was toking on joints like they were going out of business, and was soon reduced to an unconscious mess. But she hadn't tried to leave. She was resigned to her existence within this family, and that was probably the saddest realisation for Jackson.

He finished working on the Carrera and went to wash his hands. He walked past a coil of rope that he used to tie bikes up on his wall, and stopped. He went closer and examined the black twine. The weave and texture of the fibres looked just like the ones he'd been given by the coppers. Holy shit.

He calmed his nerves and pushed away panic. It gave him an idea.

'I think you should really get your hands dirty, Guns,' Jason said. Everybody else was high or unconscious. Jackson knew that Jason using his nickname meant he was forgiven for now.

'You need somebody clean, man. They'd be on me, you know that. You need someone untouchable.'

'I don't like untouchable no more. I need you to come in the crew. You could play both sides and I'd never know. I see you, Guns, dreaming of leaving and starting a new life. I'm not fucking stupid.'

'I never said you were stupid, man. But I'd be shit at it. I don't like drugs, I ain't raping no girls, Adam hates my guts. If something ain't broke, don't fix it. We've got history. You know me better than anyone.' He wasn't too proud to try flattery. It worked.

A smile spread slowly across Jason's face.

'There's too much heat at the moment and we need a courier tonight. You know me and Adam can't do it, and Tyrone has got to keep out of the way. I don't trust no one else. That little shit over there' – he pointed to a young lad who was wasted and mid-blackout – 'he was the one who stabbed that woman with my brother. He said she bled like a fucking pig. Between you and me, fam, he fucked up. I got shit breathing on me from all sides. He got me in the shit, Guns. She was the wrong one.'

'The wrong one?'

'Long story. It was supposed to be Keira and one other, but not a proper spoilt bitch like that.'

'What can I do? The coppers found two knives in the pond.' Jackson had heard it on the radio. That was part of the problem with the Cotton brothers: they lived in a bubble.

'What?' Jason's face changed.

'Divers were in there yesterday, you didn't hear? The police released the photographs on TV today. They've sent them for forensic testing.'

'But the water would have washed them clean.' Jason tried to convince himself.

'Not so apparently, bruv. They can still lift oils and shit left by fingers. Tell me they were wearing gloves?' He nodded towards Adam and the young lad who was his partner in the crime. Jason looked at his brother.

'Fucking liability,' he said. 'Guns, I've got a proposition for you.'

Not another one, Jackson thought.

Chapter 29

Sharon Bradley checked on the women who'd gathered at the barricades. The female copper who'd told her about Keira had called her to negotiate a police presence at the makeshift blockade. At first she'd almost told her to fuck off, but then she realised that the woman was serious, and she felt important. There had been an increased police presence on the estate as a result of the stabbings, but they'd kept themselves to themselves, no doubt embarrassed about yesterday. There was a clear difference between the police involved with the murder case, run by the Porter woman, and those involved in the raids yesterday.

Unlike last night, the rapport with the coppers sent this morning had been cordial, entertaining even. They'd taken their hats off and brought cups of tea to people who'd drifted there in search of shelter. Sharon reckoned the whole of Penrith's homeless had found their way to what was now a refuge of sorts. People had donated food to be handed out, not that anyone around here could afford it. She realised that a bit of common ground brought the best out in people.

Last night, scores of people had helped construct two barriers across the two main entrances and exits to and from the estate. Tents were erected and electrical wires ran from homes. Now, fires had been lit and food had been cooked on stoves, and it looked as though they'd been protesting there for months. Home-made banners read *JUSTICE FOR KEIRA*, *MOTHERS UNITED* and *STOP KNIFE CRIME NOW*. It was a peaceful protest and the detective had told her that the police were compelled to allow them their freedom of association, freedom of assembly and freedom of speech. It didn't take a rocket scientist to understand that forceful eviction of the peaceful protesters would gain huge national attention and make the police look like thugs – again – especially with children involved. Now, journalists were turning up and asking people to pose with the coppers, which they did happily, except for a few kids who should have been at school and didn't want to get caught skipping lessons.

News travelled quickly, and a steady trickle of residents appeared, as well as people from elsewhere in Penrith and even neighbouring towns, armed with blankets, food, chairs and toys. They greeted Sharon like some kind of well-known figure, and it was clear that she was gaining a status that gave her leverage among her peers. Grief had given her power and she intended to use it wisely. She marched around with a purpose and she looked different too. Her face was fresher, her eyes alive. The attention suited her.

'You need to get some sleep, Shaz,' a woman said.

'I can't sleep. No use. I don't wanna sleep until I get the bastard who did it. Anyone heard from that boyfriend of hers yet? He's a skanky coward, that one.'

'Reckon it's him?'

'I dunno. Guns don't think so. The pigs'll find someone, but they need evidence.'

The identity of Keira's recent alleged boyfriend had been confirmed by several estate members coming forward purely because of Sharon's appeal.

'He don't wanna be found, does he? Cowardly little bastard. Police were in his flat all afternoon yesterday. I wanna know why he's hiding and who he's protecting.'

'I heard about him. He's in with the Cotton brothers, ain't he?'

'Ain't everyone?'

It was a worrying development. No one had called out the Cotton brothers before. Sharon knew that regardless of all her shouting and cursing, some people just wouldn't snitch on them, even for two hundred grand.

'If he is, fuck 'em. Come on, let's get these kids fed. What've you got there?' Sharon asked.

'Pancakes from Tesco, already filled with Nutella.'

'Bloody lovely.'

Tired and jubilant faces beamed at the prospect of treats. It was akin to a non-uniform day at school: indulgent and lawless. It broke the monotony. The day was still dewy from the morning, and ice had formed on the top of waterproof sheets, and dripped off onto the road as it melted. The smell of damp bodies had formed a cloud at the entrance of the shelter.

The women swapped anecdotes about their experiences of the local authority and the law: they complained of mistreatment, neglect, being the 'forgotten ones'.

'There's another banner in that.'

Sharon agreed.

'We're like fucking Grenfell,' another woman said. 'A disaster waiting to happen. I complained about my gas again yesterday. What if it went up when the kids are asleep?'

'Right so. We're not budging until something changes.'

Sharon shouted across the street to two coppers in uniform. 'Morning, lads! Fancy a cuppa? Looks like we'll be staying a while longer.'

Chapter 30

'You've got to hand yourself in, bruv. They're gonna find you soon enough, and it looks bad.'

'I didn't do it,' Tyrone said.

'I know, man,' Jackson said. 'The Cotton brothers will make sure you take the heat for it, though.'

'How can they do that?'

Tyrone was naïvety personified and it touched Jackson.

'Bruv, they can do what they want, just like the police. Anyone can be framed. We've got to make sure they don't pull it off. I'll take care of it. What happened?'

Growing stir-crazy, Tyrone had dared to leave the flat used for drug deals and substance use, and they sat in one to which Jackson had access. They were alone and would remain undisturbed. If the police ever came into possession of the network of addresses that were used across the estate, there would always be ones that remained anonymous and untraceable.

Tyrone told Jackson about the evening he'd spent with Keira. Things were getting serious, but for some reason, he couldn't commit himself in the way she wanted.

'She was always asking for more: more holding, more affection, more phone calls, more chat, more presents. Man, I couldn't keep up. She was pissed at me. They came from nowhere, I swear.'

'Jason and Adam?'

'Yeah, and the others. They get Keira and start saying she has it coming to her, they know what she been doing.'

'Like what?'

'That's what I said, man.'

'And what did they say?'

'They said she had to keep her mouth shut about something.'

'Did you know what?'

'Nah.' Tyrone shook his head then dropped it low. Jackson knew he was suffering. The guy had been helpless to stop the butchering of his girl. And now Jason Cotton wanted to frame him. Jackson had no doubt that the coppers used Jason just like they used him. He would be surprised if Adam was in the loop, and now Jason had realised that to survive this particular little mess, he'd have to cut his brother loose. Jason had asked Jackson to make sure that Adam was with Tyrone at the other flat, when he planned to turn them both in. He had also asked Jackson to get rid of some incriminating gear that had been left in a bedroom there. At least one knife pulled from the pond would implicate Adam in the first murder, and no one would be able to prove that he didn't carry out the second as well.

It was quite similar to what the coppers had asked Jackson to do, except they'd prefer the Cotton brothers weren't taken off the streets just yet. But that was information he planned on sharing with no one. Tyrone was his friend, but he wasn't bright and couldn't be trusted with details.

'If I turn myself in, I'll go down for something I didn't do. If I stay here, Jason will get me. I don't trust that bastard.'

'And rightly so. Neither do I.'

'So what do I do, Guns?'

'Trust no one. Stay here instead of that dive. They want you there so they can use you when the time is right.'

'But they'll find out where I am.'

'Not if I'm the only one who knows.'

'It won't take long to check.'

'They could be going round in circles for weeks. You could be in a warehouse anywhere from Penrith to Work-ington. Sit tight. I'm gonna go and see Sharon.'

'Sharon! She hates my guts.'

'Maybe she won't after I talk to her.'

Jackson left the flat, making sure there was stuff in the fridge to keep Tyrone from venturing out; his stomach ruled his head. Satisfied, he headed to the barricade, where he thought he might find her. Sure enough, she was speaking to a group of people and she looked in her element: the centre of attention and in charge.

'Guns?'

'Shaz. I know you're busy, but can I borrow you?'

'What did those coppers want? I told the detective in charge.'

'What? Who?'

'The police detective in charge of Keira's murder. She's the only one who seems decent. Did you see the appeal on TV? Why the fuck wasn't I invited to that? It should have been a joint effort. That jumped-up rich guy offering all that cash: he hasn't even had the decency to call me. We should be doing stuff like that together.'

'I don't see any banners for Ella Watson, Shaz.'

'And you won't unless they lower themselves and get over here. Anyway, the policewoman called me to try and make up for that shambles last night. She said she had nothing to do with it, so I told her about those two coppers knocking on your door.'

'So I should expect a visit from her then?'

'You got nothing to hide, Guns. I'll speak for you, you know that.'

'Thanks, Shaz. I was going to ask for your help with something. What makes you trust this policewoman?'

'Because, as far as I can tell, she's putting as much into investigating Keira's death as she is into the posh woman's.'

'How about if I told you I know where Tyrone is, and he didn't do it. I swear on my life.'

'Why doesn't he turn himself in then and tell the policewoman that?'

Jackson raised his eyebrows. 'Come on, Shaz, you know the answer to that.'

'The Cotton brothers? Why is he scared of those little shits? I'm not.'

'He's not you, Shaz. And by the way, you should be scared of them, you stupid cow.' He punched her arm gently. 'Thing is, he's being set up.'

'And you believe him?'

'I know it because I'm the one who's been asked to arrange it. The two sides are playing off against one another and I'm in the middle.'

'Sounds like a proper set-up. Who the hell are you talking about?'

'The police and the Cotton brothers. I haven't worked it out yet, but they both want the same thing.'

'You think they're responsible for killing my Keira?'

Jackson nodded.

'The police?'

'Bent coppers who want to cover up the real reason that posh woman was killed, working with Jason Cotton, who I'm sure is an informer.'

'No way! You're joking.'

'Why, Shaz?'

'Informers are stupid! All they're interested in is selling fake information. The Cotton brothers wouldn't talk to the police!'

Jackson was about to tell her that he himself worked as a criminal informant, but he changed his mind.

'I'm not talking about the regular police, I'm talking about a select few individuals who are on the take themselves. I think Keira got in the way. Tyrone said she had to keep her mouth shut about something.'

'The solicitor.'

'What?' Jackson asked.

'She was seeing a solicitor in Manchester.'

'Why?'

'I have no idea.'

'Well, let's find out.'

Chapter 31

Kelly read the forensic report from Tyrone Fenton's flat. The team had gone over the place on their hands and knees, swabbing, spraying, photographing and, finally, bagging and tagging.

All seemed in order. There was a total of three hundred and seven items of interest and it would cost a small fortune to get them all checked out in a lab. It was a fact of life that sometimes one had to weigh up the importance of the inquiry against the vast chunks of budget required to investigate properly. In an ideal world, Kelly would have her own police lab, attached to Eden House, as more crimes were solved now through DNA than any other method. But it was a pipe dream.

She noted that almost twenty of the exhibits were illegal substances, and a further ten contained drug-related paraphernalia, with the rest labelled as personal items possibly storing DNA: things like toothbrushes, hair-brushes, bed sheets, clothes and so on. Fenton's photograph, from a social media platform, had been released to the press and Kelly reckoned they were close to smoking him out. They'd also released photos of the Cotton brothers from police files and informed the public that they'd like to speak to the men as a matter of urgency. It was standard language. She felt as though she was closing in on the key individuals. She had no idea how they fitted together yet, but she would.

She studied Tyrone's photograph and noted the colour of his hair. It was a shaggy mess of ginger and chestnut, similar to the hairs found under Keira's nails, but she knew that he could easily argue in a court of law that they'd had rough sex as girlfriend and boyfriend. Any DNA evidence would lead to reasonable doubt. The same could be said if it turned out to be Fenton's skin cells under her nails. She turned to the clothes, which had all been photographed. They'd found a black hoody dumped in a washing basket in the bathroom. It was similar to the one he was wearing when he was filmed on CCTV shortly after his girlfriend's fatal stabbing, and it had been sent away to be tested. The only way they could win over a jury was if Keira's blood was apparent in excessive amounts on the clothes he was wearing on the day. Of course, the biggest red flag was his disappearance, proving that he didn't care what had happened to Keira, but that too was circumstantial only. She needed hard evidence.

She'd seen it a thousand times before and figured that, when they finally apprehended him, Fenton could say that he and Keira were casual lovers and didn't keep in touch every day. He could argue that he'd been visiting friends out of the area and hadn't heard the news. It was possible. They had enough for an arrest, but charging would be a different story altogether if they failed to find any of Keira's blood on that hoody. Unlike Ella's stabbing, Ted was in no doubt that the person who'd killed Keira would have significant amounts of her blood on them, as well as possible hand injuries.

The lab had called to say that the black fibres found on Ella Watson's blue running vest were nylon, and commonly used to make rope that had a thousand and one uses. She had a list of manufacturers and the lab had managed to pinpoint a compound in the polymer that was only added to the final product to strengthen it after 2017. It narrowed down the list of suppliers. The biggest buyer was B&Q; the rope was sold in the general hardware department by length. She had DC Emma Hide working on contacting all the local hardware stores in the area to check when the product had been sold and where. It was a mammoth task, and dull, but only dogged determination, persistence and patience would root out such a crucial link. It was Emma's forte. She had an eye for detail and she never gave up. She'd requested the CCTV from the stores in question to correlate the purchasers' details. They were looking for any person of interest on their growing list.

The office was quiet, with the odd interruption as something was brought to her attention. A casual observer might think that nothing much was being done about the slaughter of two women, but behind the scenes, in and around Penrith, Kelly had almost fifty officers gathering information, taking statements and otherwise digging for clues. The members at the golf club where Neil Ormond and Thomas Watson were members had been interviewed and had given their opinions of the Watson family and of the larger-than-life character that was the superintendent. It bugged Kelly that he was treated as something of a celebrity there.

Kelly was sitting on a wheelie chair in front of a screen in the incident room. Sometimes she worked in her office, and sometimes with everyone else. Today she wanted to be with everyone else. She leant backwards and folded her arms over her stomach as she stared at her computer. She'd done a bit of digging on Will's background – her bright star rising through the ranks – and found a few surprises.

She'd discovered not only that he had gone to school with Liam Brook, but also that he was close to being convicted of a robbery-related offence when he was sixteen years old, but had cut a deal, accepting rehabilitation in a ground-breaking experiment in youth crime and reoffending stats. There was little public support for treating offenders with anything but contempt, but these experiments that popped up occasionally were powerful. She'd never heard of this one.

It wasn't on Will's official record – and certainly not on his CV, which she'd checked alongside all the others on her team – but she'd found it when she'd searched Liam Brook's record. Liam Brook had been recruited from the same rehabilitation programme as his buddy. The authorising officer accepting the two young street scrappers into the ranks of the constabulary was none other than the senior chief inspector Neil Ormond, fifteen years ago, just before he made superintendent. She wondered what to make of the massive conflict of interest that was emerging as a pattern.

It made her dig deeper. Both junior officers had done time on the Cumbria drugs squad but moved in the same year: Will Phillips to detective and Liam Brook to squad policing.

Kelly didn't like coincidences.

A creeping feeling settled under her ribcage. She'd asked around and she knew that Will had been paired with PC Brook on Op Eagle. Of course they had been: they were best muckers. She wondered who else it could have been that was so interested in Jackson Akers. Sharon had been sure that two officers had been to his flat. Why? She pondered all the operations she'd shared with Will, a young man with such a great future, and it pained her. She recalled him saving her skin a couple of years back, when she'd entered a property unassisted because she knew there was a first-class bastard inside, potentially about to murder a young girl for what she knew about his organised crime network. Will had had her back and she'd pulled it off. She could easily have been investigated for malpractice; she could even have been sued by the surviving casualty. She should never have gone in alone, but she was a rookie in the area, eager to prove herself. And Will had managed to make those details disappear. He'd turned up with Armed Response later, but the timeline had been overlooked.

Now she questioned what was behind his ability to do that so smoothly. Had he had previous experience of smudging reports? They'd never discussed it. She knew he wasn't being entirely honest with her.

Rob leant back in his chair and it made Kelly look up.

'Boss, it's quite clear from several eyewitnesses to yesterday's cock-up that two offices went into Jackson Akers' flat yesterday to talk to him.'

'ID?' She knew what was coming. Will had left the office to buy his lunch.

'One was well known on the estate for being a bit of a heavy bastard at times. His name is PC Brook.'

'And DS Phillips was paired with Brook.'

Rob didn't say anything; he didn't have to. Kelly could see in his eyes that any shred of trust he'd had for their colleague was evaporating.

'Have you checked to see if it's on HOLMES?' she asked.

'It's not.'

Emma interrupted them. 'I see we're famous, boss.' She nodded to the seventy-two-inch flat-screen TV on the wall. Rob reached for the remote to turn up the volume. It was an interview on Sky with the Shadow Home Secretary, a character always on the lookout for ways to sully the government.

'We've made our position clear time and time again: this government refuses to address the real issues facing the British public. People don't want to hear bickering and ego-jostling over Brexit: they want to see knife crime reduced, they want to know that their NHS is safe, they want the politicians to do what they were elected to do!'

The politician was animated and forceful and it was a powerful display. The ineffectiveness of current leaders had left vast swathes of vacuous opportunities in modern politics, and MPs like this one had stepped up to fill them. She was tipped to become leader within five years, and then prime minister soon after. A strapline scrolled along the bottom of the screen: *Barricades in Cumbrian city against knife crime*. In smaller letters, the two murders were described for those new to the crisis.

Kelly was so engrossed in the news unfolding that she was unaware of the crowd gathering behind her. Admin staff, uniforms and security guards alike stood and watched the TV report.

The screen divided in two and the Mayor of London took the right-hand side, giving her opinion on how best to tackle the growing spate of fatal stabbings now spilling out of London and into the provinces. It was like a sickness, infecting everything in its path. The office was transfixed. No one made a sound.

When the interviews were finished: 'We believe that the government continues to fail the people of this country by channelling unnecessary money into the pockets of their own, and neglecting the clear wishes of the voters: to tackle, head on, the desperate fight on our streets of kids knifing one another to death...'

'London has led by example and knife crime is under control—'

'That is erroneous, disingenuous and, frankly, dangerous...' the shadow minister butted in.

The spat turned into a full-on fight and the interviewer struggled to keep the two women calm.

Kelly stretched. 'Heat's turning up. That's for sure. I reckon we might get a bit more help than we need.' She turned around and noticed the people gathered behind her. 'If they really gave a crap, they'd be visiting the town to see the situation for themselves.'

Her colleagues nodded and grumbled to one another and started to disperse. Kelly went to her office to call Ormond.

'Kelly! News?'

'We're making progress, sir. My main concern is what's being said in the national press. Have you seen the latest flag-waving from the opposition and the London mayor?'

'I'm watching it now. And before you ask, yes, we've had directives issued from the Home Office. You do your job, DI Porter, and I'll do mine. You're the SIO on this case – for now – and that doesn't involve policy direction from the Met or the Home Office, as far as I remember the limitations of your rank, that is.'

Bastard.

'Yes, sir.'

'I'll keep you informed of anything you need to know, and I'd like a full report on the efforts in place to find this Fenton chap, by close of play today. He seems to be at the centre of everything. I'm also considering splitting the investigation, and handing the Potton Park murder to somebody else. It's frankly too much for you. You can concentrate on the Beacon Estate woman.'

'You mean Keira Bradley, sir?'

'Whatever.'

'Sir, I strongly advise against a split. It would affect the strength and fluency of our inquiries.'

'Really, Porter? Well if that's the case, prove it by five p.m.' He hung up.

Kelly stared at her phone. It all felt wrong. Her senior officers were supposed to trust her and support her. She'd proven herself on so many occasions since moving back from London. Her first case here had been huge: she'd taken down gangs from Ireland to Sarajevo, saving hundreds, possibly even thousands of young women from trafficking and prostitution. Her head spun. Why did she feel so powerless?

She walked back to the incident room in a semi-daze, looking around at the faces of her team. They gave their all to the job, sacrificing time with their families and friends to chase leads and catch bastards. Now it seemed as though those bastards were infiltrating her sanctuary and she didn't know who to trust. Rob and Emma looked at her with concern, and for a brief moment she questioned even their loyalty. She felt sick. Her world was crumbling.

'Boss? Emma's found something you need to see.' Rob was talking to her. She gathered herself and nodded.

'In private,' she said.

They walked back to her office and Emma opened her Toughpad: a tablet protected with a very thick cover.

'What is it?' Kelly asked.

'I've been doing what you asked, boss, and pursuing forensics. When I was searching for sales of the black rope, I came across a glut of them in B&Q in Penrith. I thought it was as good a place to start as any. They date from May to July this year. I requested the CCTV and it's digital so it was really quick. I got through five hours, and then I saw this.'

Emma turned the Toughpad around and showed Kelly a still photo from a checkout.

'Is that Jackson Akers?' Kelly asked.

'Yes.'

'Jesus, does the time correlate with the sale of the rope?'

'Yes. But that's not what I wanted to show you. I fast-forwarded to the wrong time by accident, but I found this.' She showed Kelly once more.

'What the fuck?'

On Emma's screen was a video clip of Jackson Akers talking to two men. One was Will Phillips and the other was Liam Brook.

Chapter 32

Kelly gripped the steering wheel. Rob talked as she drove towards the Beacon Estate. Emma had wanted to go with her but Rob had insisted and Kelly hadn't fought it. From social media they'd put together a detailed profile of Jackson Akers. She would have interviewed him yesterday if Op Turkey hadn't derailed her. Now was as good a time as any, and he was a big man.

'Why not just ask Will outright, boss?' Rob wanted to do everything properly, and Kelly commended his purity. Unfortunately, she didn't have the same respect for the processes she'd sworn to protect. They were letting her down; everything she'd based her ethics on was unravelling, and she knew that somehow Will was involved.

'We have to be discreet, Rob. Don't discuss this with him. It's my job to get to the bottom of it. If I go in heavy now, I could lose a chance to find out what's going on.'

'It's clear, boss. Will uses informants without your knowledge, with his pal.'

'But I need to find out who he gives the information to, because it's clearly not me.'

'Do you think he's a plant?'

'It's possible.'

There were units in the police, usually under Counter-Corruption and Surveillance, that planted officers to investigate accusations. But Kelly couldn't think why one would be embedded in her team.

'I want to tail both of them, but I can't go through Ormond.' She was thinking aloud.

'Boss?'

'Something's not right. I'm not sure if something is going on between the constabulary and the Beacon Estate gangs: namely the Cotton brothers. It makes absolute sense to me that only a close relationship between the two, and several informers – one of whom seems to be our pal Jackson – could keep a lid on tensions getting out of hand. I know from a colleague of mine in Barrow that certain areas there were too hot for police to go into. They had an operation that lasted sixteen months before they began to piece together who was who. How do we know all the players so effortlessly here in Penrith? Why is there no active investigation into the Cotton brothers? I certainly can't find one. Liam Brook told me vaguely that they keep an eye on them. I just don't know who to trust.' It was out before she could take it back. Rob understood immediately.

'You can count on me, boss. I'm not bent.'

'I know I can count on you and Emma, and Kate. But it might not end well. If this goes as high as I suspect, I won't be able to control what happens next. I've already been threatened by Ormond regarding my job.'

Ordinarily she wouldn't dream of discussing her career with a junior officer, but this was different and Rob was like a friend. She'd thought the same about Will.

'I might need to move you around to protect you. If I go down for any reason, I don't want you guys with me.'

'With your permission, ma'am. I refuse. I'm with you all the way.'

Kelly caught a glimpse of Rob's expression and turned back to the road ahead. She knew he meant it.

When they arrived at the Beacon Estate, they were both stunned at how extensive the barricades had grown. They seemed almost semi-permanent. More journalists had turned up, flags had been made, and crowds of people were listening to speeches from individuals who might or might not be from the estate: they could have been drafted in. Kelly had to take a long detour around the protests and parked behind Wordsworth Towers.

She had done her homework on Jackson Akers. At twenty, he had his whole life ahead of him, but it had come at a price. Kelly never stopped experiencing the desperation of the youngsters at the centre of most of her cases. You were born into shit: you did shit. However, that wasn't the case with Jackson Akers. He'd surprised her.

By the age of five, Jackson was fatherless, but by all accounts the boy was better off without him. By the age of ten, he was motherless. She'd disappeared as a hardened alcoholic and presumed prostitute somewhere on the streets of Glasgow. The missing person case was closed in 2012. Young Jackson lived in various children's homes during the next five years; Kelly already knew that two of those homes were underwritten by a charity run by the men at the centre of Tombday: Colin Day and Barry Crawley. She also knew that the homes were at the centre of a child abuse scandal, though that was before Jackson would have been there.

The interesting note on Jackson, though, was that he had no criminal record. Despite his past, and a glaring anomaly, Jackson Akers was clean. But then so was Tyrone Fenton.

Was it in return for being informers?

It was odd.

They saw a few curtains twitch as they made their way towards the stairwell. Kelly was only slightly apprehensive, given the events of yesterday and the injuries sustained by the two officers. The attack had been brazen and sent a clear message: the police weren't welcome on the Beacon Estate. She'd managed to thaw Sharon Bradley and convince her that investigators were different to squad patrols and didn't charge around like bullies with battering rams.

She pulled her collar up. The sky swirled grey and warned them they were on alien territory. They moved quickly. The stairwell was gloomy; Kelly wondered if concrete somehow actually sucked the life out of humans, damning them to a life of despair. Would it be any different if they were surrounded by fields and open sky, instead of these upright coffins, airtight, depressing and cold?

From the balcony they could view the barricades below. Kelly was impressed. They came to the door of the flat occupied – on paper – by Jackson Akers and knocked, looking around them as they waited. The wind took Kelly's jacket and it flapped noisily. There was no answer. Kelly knocked again. They both became aware of another figure on the balcony and turned to see Jackson standing at the end. He'd just come up from below and they'd caught him unaware, which was what they wanted; however they now didn't know if he would walk towards them or run. The two men sized each other up. Rob was a fair build: he worked out and took care of himself. But Jackson was massive.

Kelly looked at Jackson and extended her hand.

'Jackson? I'm Kelly Porter, I'm in charge of the murder inquiries. We haven't yet met.' She was calm. Rob said nothing. Jackson continued to stare, and then he looked over the balcony. He seemed to be gazing towards the area where Keira had died, and beyond, to an open area between the flats. Was he looking to see if he was being watched? There was nothing Kelly could do should that be the case, only hope he'd talk to them. The people below were noisy, and songs were played over PA systems. Laughter and banter floated up to where they waited.

At last Jackson walked towards them and pulled a key out of his pocket. His hands were dirty with what Kelly suspected was bike oil. She wondered what he'd used the black rope for. His face was open, but she'd sat in front of plenty of killers who'd tried to suck her in with their calm. Her mind remained open. All investigators knew that during a live case, it was highly probable that they'd come face to face with the killer before they knew it.

Jackson was now level with them, and he put his key in the lock, opening the door and inviting them in.

'I already talked to your lot,' he said.

'Sorry, I haven't seen a record of it. Sometimes during such large operations different departments investigate several elements of crime. I'm in charge of the murder inquiry, and I believe the officers you met yesterday were investigating general organised crime on the estate, under different orders.'

Jackson stopped and turned round. Kelly entered the hallway and Rob followed, closing the door behind him.

211

They filled the little space. Jackson pointed to a small lounge.

'Sit down if you want,' he said. They went in and did so. Jackson followed them and did the same. He was relaxed.

'Can you confirm if your interview with PC Brook and DS Phillips was recorded?'

'I don't know, they never said.'

Confirmation of identity at least.

'We have evidence linking you strongly to the scene of the murder of Keira Bradley.'

'What? Am I under arrest?' Jackson sat opposite them. Kelly noted the tidiness of the flat.

'No. I don't want to get bodies in cells, Jackson, I want to know the truth.' Kelly knew he was puzzled. She also knew he wasn't stupid. To stay out of trouble on the Beacon Estate as a young male was no mean feat. She was interested to find out how he'd managed it.

'You have a long history with DS Phillips and PC Brook.'

Jackson's face didn't change, but his hand position did, moving from his knees and clasping.

'Am I under caution?'

'No.' Kelly waited.

Jackson looked from one to the other. 'I can never work out who out of you lot is dirty and who's clean.'

'That's an odd statement. I don't work with any dirty officers.'

Jackson laughed. 'You're clean. That's nice. I could talk to you but I might suffer a nasty accident.'

'So you're telling me that you're in contact with what you call "dirty officers" and that if you talked to me and told me the truth, your life would be in danger? From whom?' Kelly remained calm, but what she heard terrified her. She sensed that Rob was struggling to keep quiet next to her.

'Both sides, man.'

Kelly let the Americanism go. All these young studs spoke the same. She found it sad, but expected. She just wished that the Caribbean twang wasn't so wrapped up with bravado and status amongst young men.

'Rival gangs?' She knew that wasn't what he meant. He shook his head.

'They might as well be,' he said.

'DC Shawcross.' Kelly turned to Rob, and he opened his Toughpad and showed the images to Jackson. The young man swallowed. Kelly admired his mettle: it was obvious that he was used to playing a dangerous game of poker with his knowledge and choices. Despite his age, he reminded her of seasoned criminal informants she'd worked with in London. 'That's you and the two officers who were here last night, isn't it?'

Jackson nodded. 'You wired?'

'No, that's for the movies. It wouldn't be admissible in court and frankly we haven't got the money. How long have you been meeting with the two officers?'

'Years, man.'

'Why?'

'Whatever they want.'

'Such as?'

He blew through his lips, sat back and spread his hands. 'Names, places, deals, gear.'

'Gear?'

'You know, where stuff's kept when it's hot.'

'Drugs? Money? People?'

'Anything.'

'And what do you get out of it?'

Jackson raised his eyebrows. 'You think I benefit from this? They just leave me alone.'

'But you've got no record; what could they possibly have on you?'

'They can plant whatever they like. I wouldn't stand a chance.'

'That doesn't happen in the force. It might—'

'Are you for real? What fuckin' planet you on?'

'I wouldn't go down that path, fella.' Rob sat up taller.

Jackson looked at him. 'I ain't being rude, but you bare stupid to think anyone has choices here. I survive.'

'Maybe it's time you changed sides.'

'Maybe, innit.'

'Did you have anything to do with the murders of Ella Watson or Keira Bradley?'

'No.'

'Do you know who did?'

'Yes.'

Chapter 33

Jordan Watson pulled up his hood. The family home was suffocating. There were too many people visiting with their sympathy faces. Dad was holed up in a chair, receiving grieving relatives and friends. It was depressing and utterly pointless. The only thing that would help was getting out and doing something. He couldn't bear Millie's tears any more either. It wasn't that she annoyed him, just that he knew he couldn't do anything about it. He couldn't do the one thing that would make all the pain go away: bring Mum back.

When he thought of Mum, his head went fuzzy and his chest tightened. The anger in his heart burned fiercely and was growing bigger by the hour. It was all-consuming and threatened to explode into a physical manifestation against somebody he loved if it wasn't dealt with. To exorcise it he had to move. Sitting in the house helped no one. Reminiscing, like Millie, giving up like his father, or constant swooning, like Grandma, didn't meet his own individual need: the desire for revenge.

He'd asked around and found out where most of his friends got their recreational drugs. Parties were stuffed with illegal substances at their age, and if their parents knew the extent of the use and availability, they'd no doubt keel over, shocked and horrified. They thought kids did what kids had always done: fool around, make jokes, act like idiots and cause a little trouble. None of the parents he or his friends knew would believe the amount of drugs and alcohol consumed by his generation. The press said that his age group was turning its back on mind-altering substances. But that wasn't what he saw. Every party was super charged with an 'olders' network, oiled to perfection with practice and experience, ready and stocked for exchanges between various dealers in drugs, alcohol and cigarettes. Sixth-formers dealt the alcohol, most teenagers could get the cigarettes, and anyone could get drugs: from ket tablets to simple zoots of weed. He knew plenty of Year 7 students – barely eleven years old – hooked on it all. Teachers knew nothing. Parents knew nothing.

But that wasn't why he was here. He was here to score, though only ostensibly; what he really wanted was to become involved. He cared nothing for how long it took him. He'd use his wit and his charm to find his way in, and when he did, he'd get his revenge.

The Beacon Estate was a shithole. However, Jordan thought it might be a safer place to exist than in his current world, where the pressure to act in a certain way was as stifling as the misery shrouding his home right now. Here, he figured, he could become anonymous. He could fall below the standards of his father and disappear. The thought was arousing. The experience of walking free through the estate, answerable to no one, unsure of what might happen next, gave him the stimulant he'd been looking for for years. The constraints of exams, job profiles, the Duke of Edinburgh award, jumping through hoops and living a life that amounted to nothing at all when it was broken down into pieces, as it had been this week, were tearing him apart.

He had nothing to lose.

And everything to gain.

He spotted a group of kids in a park and went over to them. He spoke his best gangster language. Everybody spoke like that when they were with their mates, so it wasn't difficult to appear natural. It didn't matter how respectable the family: all kids learned from the same rap and drill. His mother had never heard him speak in such a way, except when she caught him singing along to rap on YouTube in his room. She'd said he was good at it, but she wouldn't tell Dad.

Cutting a deal was the easiest thing he'd done all year. One kid on a bike offered to cycle to get some gear and he had to wait with the others. While he waited, he asked questions he'd prepared earlier, doing it in such a way that he was actually gleaning information from the small group of youngsters without them even realising it. He picked up names, flats, gathering places and recent reviews of certain inflammatory events on the estate.

'Where yuz from, bruv?'

'Manchester. Seeing cousins, innit. Fucking boring.'

The boys laughed and shared a smoke with the stranger.

'Yuz around for long?'

'Dunno.'

Jordan asked for a go on one of the younger boys' BMX. He knew some tricks. He jumped on the bike and sped down the street; from the end, he could see the barricades and the demonstrators holding banners and chanting. He raced back to the boys and pulled a spinning wheelie in front of them. He'd perfected it as part of learning a new skill for his Duke of Edinburgh silver award. He set off again and flipped the bike into the air, landing on the road with the bike perched on a wall. The boys whistled.

'That's sick,' one said. Jordan genuinely warmed to them. The boy came back with his gear and they traded happily.

'Thanks, man.'

'Come with us, man, we're going to get high tonight.'

'Where?'

'Ah, just at my mate's, he deals the ket round here.'

'Where's he get it from? Manchester?'

'Nah, man, we have our own suppliers. Don't need no Mancs, bruv!'

'County lines, innit. Should've known.'

'Yeah, you're the enemy, bruv, we doin' yuz a favour.'

'I know, man. Thanks. I'll come if that's OK?'

Jordan was allowed to hang around and he knew that was his invitation sorted. He puffed gently on a spliff and made a note to himself to be careful not to get too genuinely high. He needed a clear head so that he could gather information. He'd put into place all the security measures he could think of: he had no ID, no traceable phone – he'd bought a pay-as-you-go – no credit card, and he'd ditched his bus pass. Should anyone be suspicious – which he doubted – the last thing he needed was to be identified and vulnerable in a place like this. By the time he was led through the streets, past the demonstration, the media and the fires to keep them warm, he'd developed an affection for the boys he was with, who'd taken him in so easily. He felt part of a tribe and it gave him a sensation of belonging that he hadn't known before. He kept checking his pockets for the cash he'd brought with him, just in case he got sloppy, or someone spotted it. He'd stuffed around three hundred quid from his savings account into his various pockets, along with two knives from the kitchen block.

Afternoon turned to night-time quickly at this time of year, and the street lighting on the estate was random. Some of the bulbs were smashed out, and he felt as though he was being led through a maze of underground tunnels, on a top-secret mission. He supposed he was. They relied on their phones sometimes for light, and the ends of their cigarettes or rollies. The smell of weed filled the air and Jordan could feel himself becoming a little intoxicated with the substances he'd put into his system.

'Fuckin' pigs.' One of the boys nodded to the police tape surrounding where Jordan supposed Keira Bradley had died. They'd gone past a few coppers, who'd bizarrely greeted them with a 'good afternoon, lads'. He was puzzled, because Neil Ormond had promised his dad he was coming down hard on those responsible. Maybe it was the response to the heavy-handed raids of yesterday that had changed their tactics. The police he saw were more interested in keeping the demonstrations calm, rather than in teenagers going to a party.

At one corner, though, two coppers stopped them and asked if they knew anything about certain characters who'd been brought to their attention. They had pictures of faces, and showed them to the small group. All the youngsters with Jordan denied any knowledge of them. Jordan memorised their names: Tyrone Fenton, Jason Cotton and Adam Cotton. He'd heard about the Cotton brothers before, but now he feared they might be involved. This was as serious as it got. He'd expected to be dealing with some small-town drug addicts, not the people in charge.

'Where you off to?' the officers asked them.

'Home.'

'Where's that, lads?'

'Up there.'

They made their way up a stairwell, and Jordan noticed the name of the block: Wordsworth Towers. They approached a door and knocked, being let in after recognition and a quick conversation. The interior was as black as oil, and they were led through a series of further doorways, finally going upstairs to a large room with dozens of people crammed into it. The music was pretty loud and aggressive. Jordan glanced around with a slightly clearer head: he hadn't taken any substances for a good twenty minutes, and hadn't been inhaling the ganja properly. There was a moving mass of bodies in front of him, and as his eyes adjusted, he saw that groups were dancing, writhing, singing, smoking and moving together, generally celebrating the freedom from reality that came with a drug-addled brain. Through the smoke and dark he could make out figures in dark corners performing sex acts, seemingly unfazed by the backdrop to their activities. It was illicit, like nothing he'd ever witnessed for real, and it excited him.

The throbbing air simultaneously pressurised and relieved the fluid in his head, and worked to mesmerise him into a rhythm of beating and pulsating. He found himself falling deeper and deeper into the feeling of the moment. His body began to move and he danced against three girls next to him. He caught the eye of one of them and she made it clear that she wanted him. Her hand felt around his back and he sank his head towards hers. She kissed him openly and fully and he felt a thrill race up his body. He closed his eyes and she pressed against him. They moved together as one.

The deep, guttural bass pervaded every other sound as it dropped like a stone, rhythmic and repetitive. The words came in between each steady boom. Electric vibration lingered inside the eardrums, shaking the floor and making people move as one. Boys flicked their hands in synchronicity as a flow of words streamed from their mouths. Most of them knew the words verbatim. Jordan was familiar with the artist playing and could rap along like the others, making him appear more authentic. The words came like bullets and the melody was in the delivery not the music. Everyone mumbled along.

Don't @ me. Blast the skeng.

Emphasis was heaped on the rise and fall of the lyrics. Girls in dark corners raised their arms.

You know I blast the skeng.
Free my guys from out the pen.

A group of youths created a core group of dancers jumping up and down to the rhythm.

Big man drillz.
I don't bare pop pills.

It was clear that a crescendo was coming. Jordan watched as the mass prepared to sing the chorus. The jerking and leaping intensified.

At this point, the whole room erupted and sang 'holla, hello, hey', rising and falling as one brotherhood, arms in the air, hoodies nodding. Jordan watched and joined in. He opened his eyes to look at the girl, and she smiled, holding tightly on to him as they jumped. As the music pulsed on, she beckoned him to another room. On his way out, he noticed a tight group in intense conversation. Like most males in the room, they wore hoods, and some had bandannas over their mouths. A couple of them nodded to the girl. She pulled his hand and he found himself in front of the group. It seemed quieter over there, and the buzz of the music and the electricity he imagined coming from the girl's body dissipated.

'Come on, Adam, leave us alone,' the girl said to one of the men.

'You rubbin' up one o' mine, bruv, and I don't know yuz.'

Jordan sobered up. He felt something against his back and suspected it was a blade. He thought of his mother.

'I'm not carrying a shank, bruv. I'm staying in the tower with cousins. I came with them.' He pointed to the group of youngsters. One of them noticed and came over.

'He's sick, man,' he said. 'Nuffin' goin' on, swear it. He's safe. Calm.'

Adam smiled, then glanced over Jordan's shoulder and shook his head. The item sticking into his back was removed.

'Enjoy fuckin' her, man, she's hot.'

The girl took his hand and led him away. Jordan could feel that he was shaking. And he was no longer aroused.

222

He wanted to stay and get to know Adam. He wanted to study his body and work out where to stick a blade so that it would fucking hurt. She led him to a mattress in the corner of the next room and fell onto it, pulling him on top of her. She was high or drunk, or both, and Jordan looked at her differently now. He held back, but she took his hand and kissed him. The music came back to him, and without thinking any more, his body responded to her. She took her top off and he stared at her. She was beautiful. Anyone else in the room was forgotten. Within seconds, she was fully naked and he was inside her.

Every fibre of his body galloped towards a precipice that had opened up two days ago and remained elusive ever since. Here and now, he ran towards it at full speed. The music, the rhythm, the thump of feet, the screams of dancers, the thud of bodies falling over and the heat all colluded to help him towards the edge, and over it. He fell, head first, blind, numbed, alive, dead and on fire.

The only thing he saw as they lay together gasping for air, chests heaving and bodies slippery with sweat, was the face of the guy called Adam.

Chapter 34

Four blocks away, armed police were preparing to enter a flat. They'd been tipped off that Tyrone Fenton was hiding there. Kelly liaised closely with the firearms chief. It was fully within her power to direct the operation once she'd gained authority to use armed officers. That authority had come from a colleague the same rank as Neil Ormond in Ormond's absence, and Kelly knew it was a stroke of luck. She'd been informed that the superintendent had requested not to be disturbed as he was visiting his friend Thomas Watson at his home. It meant that she could do her job undisturbed. For the moment.

The officers moved into place after a thorough tactical meeting about the pitfalls and snagging points in the area around the flats. From where they waited, they could hear the vague thud of music, but it was not unexpected or unusual. Otherwise, apart from the barricades, which had grown larger throughout the day, the estate was fairly quiet. The rear of the property had already been secured. From her position in the stairwell, Kelly approved the entry at the front, and this was corroborated by the firearms chief. There was a sudden flurry of activity as the officers stormed forward and bashed in the flimsy door, running inside and shouting orders.

'Get down! Lie down! Don't move! Armed police!'

There was an agonising wait of around half a minute, and then:

'Suspects apprehended. Repeat, suspects apprehended. Property secure.'

Kelly let out the breath she'd been holding and went up to the second-floor flat, hoping to meet Tyrone Fenton face to face as he was arrested on suspicion of the murder of Keira Bradley and cautioned. She walked towards the bashed-in door and went inside. The flat smelled stale, of smoke and unwashed bodies. She followed the noise and found a man on the floor, being cuffed by police. The officers from the firearms unit were stood down; it was always a relief that no one had been hurt.

'He confirmed his name, ma'am.'

'Thank you.'

It wasn't Tyrone Fenton.

The man on the floor struggled, but the uniform cuffing him was twice his size and easily flipped him over and onto his feet. The young man stared at the officer and stood still. Kelly looked around. Six arrests had taken place, none Tyrone. The suspects would now be loaded into vans and the police would have twenty-four hours to interview them under caution.

She looked for wounds on any of the apprehended men's hands; there were none. They all had the hallmarks of hardened criminals: unfazed at arrest, resistance, arrogant stares and silence.

The forensic team arrived.

She looked at her watch. Ormond's threat was either just that, or he'd forgotten. He'd said 5 p.m. to get some answers for him, but that deadline had come and gone and he hadn't bothered her. It was Friday night and he'd probably gone home early to start his weekend, or that was what she hoped.

They all needed a break. She'd ordered Rob home to check on Mia. Tomorrow was the weekend, but during a murder investigation, time became irrelevant. However, they still needed to look after themselves. She didn't expect any of them back in the office tonight, except Emma Hide, who was working the late shift. The interviews of the men apprehended at the flat today would probably take place tomorrow now, as lawyers would have to be found for all of them. She was looking forward to getting to Ted's to spend some time with her loved ones. She also needed a shower.

Chapter 35

Kelly walked wearily to her car and called Johnny, who confirmed they were all waiting for her at Ted's cottage. The last thing she wanted was to be an honoured guest, but sometimes it just worked out like that.

She felt faint butterflies in her tummy. The last time she'd met June and Amber was in the summer, when she'd finished a particularly tricky case. With Florida and work, they hadn't found time to see each other since then. Both her half-sisters had busy lives. June and her partner ran a chocolatier business called Silk; they'd expanded to London and Edinburgh and had been featured in a piece in the *Sunday Times*. Amber was a primary school head teacher. They were both successful women, but, most important for Kelly, they didn't take themselves too seriously. They had a buoyant and easy relationship with their father, despite their problems with their mother. It had been hard on all of them. In her line of work, Kelly saw plenty of families ripped apart by substance abuse.

A quick stop at her own house in Pooley Bridge enabled her to shower and freshen up, then she bought some flowers and a bottle of wine for her father and drove to the pretty town of Keswick, over which the mighty Skiddaw acted as sentinel. She could see its outline in the darkness. How simple to be a mountain, she thought. She parked in Ted's driveway, which was tight, space in the medieval settlement being at a premium.

Johnny opened the front door and Kelly felt the tension in her body release. She smiled as he walked towards her. He looked tanned in the light spilling out of the doorway, his life on the fells showing. His jumper fell loose about his frame, but she knew that underneath, his body was hard. That wasn't what she relied on, though: it was the hardness of his mettle that was important to her, a mixture of what he'd experienced of the world as well as what he knew was possible. Like her, he saw the bare face of human nature when he rescued a stranded climber on the mountainside, but he'd seen it too when he'd stared into the eyes of a refugee in Kosovo: he understood what she was dealing with; he *got* it.

She allowed him to hold her and he kissed her forehead. He smelled clean and masculine and she wondered, not for the first time, if she should do something else with her life. They could sail away, perhaps to Florida again, and spend the rest of their lives between beach and boat. But she knew that her reality was here, with Ted and Josie and shitbags who needed catching. She smiled at him and took his hand.

'Josie thinks Amber is hilarious,' he said. 'She's been telling us stories about what little kids come out with at school about their parents.'

'Everyone relaxed?'

'Yes. Are you OK?'

'Maybe we'll get to talk about it later. I'm really looking forward to switching off for a few hours.'

They kissed, then he led her inside. Ted was at the stove, wearing a pinafore that said *Victory is in the Kitchen*.

Kelly had bought it for him in London when she'd worked down there for a week during the summer. Ted had been born after the Second World War but he wasn't too young to remember rationing.

'Kelly! Can you have some wine?'

'Yes, go on, I've given myself the evening off.' As the SIO, she'd left work for the night shift to do. They'd call her if they needed her. She could have a few glasses, with food.

'Ah, good!' He hugged her. 'Any progress?'

She paused before she answered and watched him stir something that looked and smelled divine.

'I know it's perhaps not the time...' she said.

'But...' he filled in for her. She smiled.

'Remember the Tombday case, and all the hobnobbing balls that were thrown for the senior glitterati of Cumbrian business?'

'Yes, I do. Very well. I'm not proud of it.' He had attended many of the functions in question, and had rubbed shoulders with many of Cumbria's great and good. Senior pathologists were always welcome at such celebrations. However, the Tombday case had blown the network apart and many of the old guard were now imprisoned, or dead.

'Neil Ormond. Know him?'

'Of course, the superintendent? Is he running the show?'

'Yes, but being blunt...'

'The only way to be... He likes the limelight, doesn't he? Don't tell me, he's getting in the way? He's very old school, Neil. I should imagine he's finding working with you a challenge. Not only are you a woman, but you're an incredibly talented one at that.'

'Well, thank you. I've got a problem, Dad.'

Ted stopped stirring. 'What is it?'

'I don't trust him.'

He put the spoon down and gave her his full attention. 'Your instinct is rarely off target. Is it that you don't like him or that you think he's not trustworthy?'

'I don't know. I need evidence.'

'Go easy. He's a very big fish in a little pond.'

'Can you remember him hobnobbing with Colin Day and Barry Crawley?'

Ted began stirring again, and June appeared in the doorway. She went to Kelly and embraced her. Kelly could be particular about her personal space, but she didn't find June or Amber invasive: it was genuine affection, and she hugged her back.

'It's good to see you again,' she said.

'Is this a serious conversation?' June asked.

'Just work. You look lovely, June, have you been away?'

'We had a mini break in Paris and the weather was incredible. It's a fierce market to break into, but Silk is in talks with a chocolate supplier that fulfils restaurant orders across Paris.'

'Oh my God, June! That's amazing! Come on, let's celebrate,' Kelly said.

'Open that bottle of bubbly in the fridge, girls,' Ted said. Kelly knew it would be a good one; he only ever bought Pol Roger, Winston Churchill's favourite. 'I do remember Neil being rather friendly with that lot. It was fairly normal back then. That is a worrisome development, but let's pursue it another time.'

Kelly opened the champagne and the cork flew into the ceiling with a pop. She filled two glasses, then took the bottle into the lounge.

'What's the occasion?' Amber asked, giving her a hug.

'June was just telling me about Paris.'

'I'll drink to that!' Amber fetched more flutes and Johnny accepted a glass, allowing Josie and Callum one too.

'Don't worry,' Ted shouted, 'I've got more!'

With the pleasantries over, Amber continued her story of a five-year-old who'd taken a shit in the school sandpit. Kelly wanted to catch up and listen to all of their stories. She wanted to pretend that her life was normal, just for an evening. But inevitably, conversation soon got round to the two murders. All anyone wanted to know about was the inquiry and the demonstrations on the Beacon Estate.

'It's opened a real can of worms. The two women were so different, and sadly, that has been at the forefront of the inquiries.'

'The press are almost saying that Ella Watson should never have had her life ended in such a manner, but because Keira Bradley lived in the grinding cycle of deprivation, her death was inevitable. It's disgusting,' said Amber.

Ted brought in canapés and serviettes. Kelly took some and passed the plate along. She munched happily on the little balls of joy on the end of a cocktail stick and realised that she hadn't eaten all day. That was probably where her dehydration headache had come from. Instead of taking on water, she'd popped paracetamol at work. Now she knew that her body craved sustenance and asked for the plate to be handed back. Ted said they were apricots wrapped in bacon and roasted with honey.

'What happened to our society, where kids don't dream any more?' asked June.

Kelly stared at June, who fancied herself an intellectual, and had a habit of throwing curveballs into conversations. If she wasn't so earnest, it would be clichéd.

'Is that true?' asked Kelly. 'Callum, Josie, do you have dreams?'

'I want to swim with sharks,' Callum said.

Amber whistled. 'I want to skinny-dip off a South Pacific island.'

'That's two of you who want to be eaten by sharks. No thanks.' June rejected the idea.

'I don't think it's necessarily guaranteed that if you swim naked in the Pacific you'll get eaten by a shark. I think there are good odds of not being attacked,' Callum said.

'True. More chance of being in a car crash,' Ted said.

'Or being knifed.' Josie brought the tone down, but she had a good point.

'Come on, Kelly, tell us about the cases. Have you caught anyone yet? The Home Secretary is getting an absolute panning in the press.'

Kelly smiled. 'I'm visiting the barricade tomorrow. Keira's mother – you've probably seen her on TV – has done some amazing work in pulling the community together. I've never seen anything like it. No, we haven't caught anyone yet, but these things take time: I've got to have hard evidence. It's all very well finding fingerprints and DNA, but I've got to have someone to match it to.'

'I saw her, she's quite an impressive character,' Amber said.

'She is. Why don't you visit the barricades yourselves; it really is an impressive sight. And now that Thomas Watson has offered two hundred grand for information, I'm hoping that any day now I'll have the suspects in custody.'

'Was it someone from the estate? Surely people know who they are?'

'It's not that easy. You can't make an arrest without suspecting someone has committed a crime.' Kelly tried to keep her answers generic. She didn't let on that the CCTV was virtually useless because the men covered their faces, nor did she admit that the Cotton brothers and Tyrone Fenton had gone to ground.

'I want to go to the barricades,' Callum said. 'We're reading Orwell's *Road to Wigan Pier*, studying the impact of the Great Depression on society in 1930s Britain, and I want to do a comparison to today.'

The adults in the room stared at him. Ted clapped his hands. 'Now there's ambition. Good for you, Callum! Kelly, you have to let him come with you. Or he could come with me. As chief coroner, I'll need to visit the sites again myself. What about you, Josie?'

'I don't think…' Johnny looked nervous.

'Come with us if you're worried,' Ted said. Johnny couldn't argue with that. It was sorted. They'd go en masse tomorrow and maybe Kelly would have time to see them.

'It's a movement! A social movement! That's how it's being reported in the press,' Ted said, munching on another round of nibbles, this time devilled eggs.

'The left-wing press, Dad,' June said.

Amber snorted. 'We all know you're a *Telegraph* reader, June.'

Kelly looked at the sisters and realised that it wasn't just her family who fought. She hadn't seen or spoken to her own sister for a long time, and as the gap got wider, she felt less inclined to bridge it. She had two sisters right here and she watched them bicker, enjoying their exchanges.

Ted folded his arms and sighed. 'They were like this when they were teenagers: one supported Labour, the other Tory. You'd never believe they were raised in the same household.'

'I'd never have been able to start my business under Labour!' June said.

'And under the Tories, you'll never get a pension!' Amber retorted.

'Girls!' Ted stood between them. Callum and Josie laughed at the show. Amber flicked her hand as if to say the argument wasn't worth it, and June rolled her eyes.

'Right, let's sit down and get this meal started,' Ted said. They all helped bring dishes out and squeezed around the table. When he'd bought the small cottage, Ted hadn't been expecting to entertain so many guests, but he wasn't complaining. He brought a huge pot from the kitchen and they passed plates around, serving themselves with vegetables and rice. Quiet descended on the room.

'This is lovely, Grandad,' said Josie.

Kelly stared at her, and then at Johnny, who was looking at Josie with so much love and pride that she felt a tiny flinch of regret that she didn't have a child of her own with this man.

Chapter 36

It was gone 9 p.m. when DC Emma Hide called Kelly on her mobile. She felt cosy on the sofa, surrounded by her family, after a wonderful meal and laughter to keep her soul light. Now, her stomach turned over. Emma would never disturb her if it was trivial.

Johnny and Ted looked at her simultaneously and knew what was coming.

'Guv, Jackson Akers has just walked into the station with Tyrone Fenton.'

Kelly stood up and went into the kitchen.

'What the hell?'

'They're in the interview suite. I thought you'd want to talk to them yourself. They've waived their right to a lawyer.'

'Of course, thanks, Emma, I'll be there in twenty minutes.'

She hung up.

'I'm sorry, guys, I've got to go back to the office.'

'How much have you drunk? Want me to take you?' Johnny asked. He'd only had one glass of champagne and a beer.

'Please.'

She hugged her father and everyone else in turn, promising to make this a regular occasion.

She was thankful for the opportunity to talk to Johnny in private.

'It was good to see you relax for a couple of hours.'

'It was lovely. I could do that every night of the week.'

'No you couldn't. You'd all fall out, like any family, and you'd get bored.'

She smiled, knowing that it was the fact that the evening was unusual that made it so special.

'What's up?'

'Ormond basically threatened me again this afternoon.'

'In what way?'

'Pretty directly. He keeps reminding me that he chooses the SIO on a case, and his implication leaves me thinking that if I don't do as he says, my career is in jeopardy.'

'There's only one reason to get rid of his best detective.'

'Because if I really am that good, then I'll unearth something he doesn't want getting out.'

'Have you found anything solid yet?'

'I'm looking into it. He's had associations with some unsavoury criminals in the past and I wonder how involved he was. Will seems to be well and truly in his pocket. He's been cagey with me for the first time ever, and he won't answer my questions directly. He's also been working covertly with informants, without my knowledge.'

'And you think he's doing it for Ormond?'

'Yes, but it seems to be coercive.'

'He has something on Will?'

'That's what I'm worried about. I hope not.'

'You rate Will?'

'Of course. He's part of my dream team. Maybe I've been naïve.'

They pulled up outside Eden House and kissed. Johnny told her to call him for a lift, but she said she'd get a squad car to drop her off, and not to wait up.

DC Emma Hide had been busy. The office was empty, and she told Kelly what she'd dug up.

'I'm trying to trace a shipment of contraband that was apprehended at Kendal services, in four lorries, seven years ago. It was one of the largest drug busts in recent years, not counting Barrow, of course. It was all logged and sent to various holding depots, but the trail stops dead and the paperwork doesn't add up. I can't find it beyond 2016. Each component should have been destroyed as scheduled, but I can't find confirmation that several containers were actually disposed of in the correct manner.'

'Several? Plural?' Kelly asked.

'Four full-sized containers.'

'That's a lot of contraband. Who was in charge of the operation?'

'I don't recognise the names of any of the drug squad officers, but there is a memo from HQ recommending they have executive authority over the operation because of the size of it. Lancaster was trying to muscle in too, as well as Greater Manchester, because of the provenance of the goods.'

'Which was?'

'It's unclear. North-west, I think, but Cumbria won it. The final authority checking the figures submitted by the drug squad from there on was Superintendent Ormond, who was also the senior officer overseeing every transaction and movement of the goods.'

'Where were they supposed to go?'

'Preston depot. And that's where the paperwork gets lost.'

'Jesus. What was the contraband?'

'Class A and B drugs, cash and firearms.'

Seven years ago was way before Kelly had returned to Cumbria from the Met, and she hadn't heard of this case before. She couldn't help thinking that Ormond was somehow involved with making the contraband disappear, no doubt for huge personal financial gain. Again Tombday came to mind, because part of Barry Crawley's involvement had been using his haulage company to move illegal immigrants.

'Did you notice the name of the haulage company?'

'I was getting to that. It was Crawley and Son.'

Kelly's mind wandered to London and the Coryn Boulder case, which had led to her shameful departure from a job she had loved almost four years ago. It was her first and only experience of misogynistic betrayal at the Met. But now she couldn't help thinking that she faced a similar threat. And it caused the same anxiety. In her core, she knew that Ormond was up to no good; she simply couldn't explain his behaviour any other way. Now she had something to work on. It was something to take to the counter-corruption intelligence unit.

She tried to concentrate on her job in the moment, to distract her. Worrying about everything wouldn't get them answers.

'Any new intel on where the Cotton brothers are?'

'No. But I did get a message from the lab on the bag of clothes found in Tyrone Fenton's flat. They performed a Kastle–Meyer test, and it's positive. It's blood.'

The test used the chemical phenolphthalein to detect haemoglobin.

'Encouraging. DNA profile?'

'They're working on it.'

A call came through to Kelly's personal mobile. Superintendent Ormond.

'Shit.'

She took the call with clenched fists and heart pumping. She felt sick. She'd begun to believe his threat was all hot air.

'Sir.' She spoke firmly.

'Porter.' He sounded drunk. 'What can I tell Tom Watson?'

'It's early days yet, sir.' She didn't want to let on that Tyrone Fenton had just walked into Eden House, nor did she want a lengthy exchange with an aggressive high-ranking officer under the influence.

'I've come to expect this from you, Porter. It's a bit like that case that finished you in London, isn't it? Leaving loose ends, going your own way. Find the evidence, or you're finished. You're close to suspension as it is over your bungling of the interview notes of a prime suspect.'

'Excuse me, sir?' Kelly's stomach dropped to her feet.

'Losing vital interview records; I have the report in front of me now. A technician familiar with HOLMES has confirmed that you were responsible for the interview of a key witness and potential suspect, and there's no record of it. Check your notes, Porter. Sloppy work. This is your final warning.' He hung up.

'Guv?'

Emma's voice was a low hum in her head. Kelly's hands were shaking, and it took all of her strength to compose herself. She was aware that she was crumbling in front of a junior officer and a valued member of her team. Her world was falling apart, but why? The only reason could be that she was getting too close to something.

'You all right, guv?'

Kelly looked at Emma and nodded. 'I'm sure there's been some mistake. He said I was responsible for messing up information on HOLMES. To be honest, I don't know what he's talking about. He sounded as though he was slurring his words.'

'I'm here until midnight, boss, I'll find out as much as I can about the Preston depot and the missing contraband. Are you planning to talk to Fenton and Akers?'

'Who? Oh, of course! Yes. Let's go.'

Chapter 37

Kelly and Emma walked to the lifts and took the elevator down to the interview suites. Jackson Akers and Tyrone Fenton had been asked to wait inside, and as the officers entered, Tyrone stood up. Jackson pulled him down and Tyrone sank back into his chair. Kelly studied both of them and made the introductions. She wished for an instant that Rob was here, but reassured herself that Eden House contained more than enough manpower to protect her.

Tyrone looked uncomfortable. Kelly watched Jackson for signs of deceit, trickery or game-playing, but found none.

'Jackson, do you want to enlighten me on why you've both decided to come in tonight?'

'Tyrone heard that you guys were looking for him, you know; about Keira.'

At the mention of the dead girl, Tyrone looked down and closed his eyes. Kelly noticed that he had his sleeves pulled over his hands.

'Tyrone? Why do you think we want to talk to you?'

''Cause she was my girl, and I ran away.'

'Why did you run away?'

'I was told to!'

'By whom?'

Tyrone looked at Jackson and Kelly thought he might bottle it and change his mind about whatever he'd come here to tell her.

'Jason Cotton.'

'And why did he tell you to run?'

'He told all of us to lay low, else we'd be taken down for Keira's murder.'

'Did you kill Keira?'

'No, man! I did not!'

Kelly stayed calm, encouraging the same from Tyrone.

'Do you know who did kill her?'

Tyrone nodded.

'Were you a witness?'

He nodded again and sniffed, wiping his sleeve over his nose. Kelly caught a glimpse of a cut on his left hand.

'Who did it?'

'Jason.'

'And you saw it?'

Tyrone nodded.

'Are you willing to testify?'

Another nod. Jackson patted his friend on the back.

Tyrone carried on. 'Jason gave me his clothes and the knife, and told me to disappear for a while.'

'Do you have them?'

Jackson produced a bag from under his jumper. Kelly couldn't believe what she was seeing.

'Would you be willing to supply a DNA sample and fingerprints to rule you out, Tyrone?'

Tyrone glared at Jackson, then back at Kelly, and nodded. Emma took a swab from a box and rubbed it around his mouth. They could do the prints later.

'Why did Jason do it, Tyrone?'

'He said he was told to, but he didn't know why. It happens. I tried to stop him.'

'And that's how you got that cut on your hand?'

Tyrone touched the wound self-consciously and nodded.

'Who told him to do it?'

'Dunno.'

For the first time, Kelly didn't believe him.

'When you say "it happens", do you mean that Jason often kills or maims to order?'

Tyrone looked at Jackson. 'She means does Jason take orders and carry them out?'

Jackson turned to Kelly and said that he did.

'Who else?'

'Adam, his brother.'

'What about Ella Watson?'

Jackson and Tyrone exchanged glances.

'We don't know nuffin' about that one,' Tyrone said.

'That one? It sounds like they were both contracts. Is that the case?'

'Could be,' Tyrone said.

'Why, though? We can't find any reason to take out Ella. There simply is no motive, unless...' Kelly fell silent and looked at Jackson. 'Unless it was a mistake.'

Jackson moved his head almost imperceptibly up and down, but Kelly saw it and she locked eyes with him.

'They had to take out somebody but took her out by mistake, thinking they were doing the right thing, to make it look like a senseless killing. Did Jason do that too?'

'I think it was his brother. Adam's a loose cannon. Jason beat him half to death for something and I think that's what it was. On Wednesday afternoon, I saw Adam

243

and he was stoned. He was with another guy and they looked like they were wound up, you know? Buzzing about something.'

'That still doesn't tell me why they were looking for someone to stab. When you say Adam's a loose cannon, do you mean he's killed randomly before?'

Jackson thought about it. 'I never heard him attack no one for no reason; it was always a rival, for drugs or a girl.'

'None of that applies to Mrs Watson. Why are you telling me all this? You're both guilty of withholding information, and Tyrone, you were party to murder.'

'We thought we could make a deal.' Jackson spoke quietly and Kelly understood how hard this was for him to admit. He was a young man who'd got away with his life on so many occasions, toeing the line and informing police, but now he was in too deep. The error – if she could prove it – in killing Ella Watson was causing calamitous ripples for the whole Cotton network on the Beacon Estate. But these two men trusted her and she felt deep remorse that she might not be able to protect them. If Ormond took her off the case, anything could happen.

'Tyrone, tell me what happened on Thursday morning.'

He began slowly and quietly, telling a story of two young people who'd partied all night, having sex, smoking drugs, being carefree. Then he described how it all ended, with Keira being held from behind and Jason stabbing her. Kelly had read the autopsy; she knew Keira had been stabbed eleven times in the gut. It sickened her. But these men sitting before her had nothing to gain and everything to lose. Tyrone would never have walked in here if it wasn't for Jackson. And Jackson would never have walked in here if it wasn't his last resort. She had to find some way to reward them.

'Can I take the bag?'

'The knife's in an envelope.'

She put on plastic gloves and found the envelope, peering inside at a small knife that looked as though it should be used for peeling potatoes. It matched what Ted had told her about the weapon that had ended Keira's life.

'Is there anything else you came to tell me tonight? Do you know where the brothers are?'

'I know loads of the places they use,' Jackson said.

'I'm listening.'

Chapter 38

Thomas Watson looked at the man in front of him. He'd never really considered him a close friend, but he was grateful for his help – or so he'd thought. Neil Ormond had just got off the phone with DI Porter, and Thomas didn't like the tone he'd used with her. As far as Thomas was concerned, Kelly Porter was a thoroughly decent and genuine person. Millie in particular thought the woman kind and warm. Yet here in his house, under the influence of alcohol, her boss was telling him otherwise.

Thomas hadn't invited Ormond; he'd just turned up. He'd occasionally shared a pint with the man at the golf club, and they'd been over for Sunday lunch once. As they'd left, Ella had told him that she was unsure of Ormond and not convinced that he was cut out to be a senior policeman: she didn't get the impression that his morals were sound.

When Thomas had questioned her, she'd said that Neil had come out with a few things that she found inappropriate and frankly disturbing. He'd made a joke about something in the news involving children, and she didn't like the way he slapped his wife's rear.

'Women's intuition,' she'd said.

The irony sat heavy on his heart: that the man Ella had harboured distaste for was in her kitchen now, ranting about her possible killers. Thomas couldn't figure out why Ormond was so crazed over Ella's case. He'd talked of a young man called Tyrone, and promised that he'd be apprehended and locked up before Christmas; it was wild talk for somebody who represented an institution so tightly regulated and in the spotlight. In the good old days of bobbies on the beat, where crime was settled on the street, perhaps Neil would have fitted in, but now, any tiny mistake made by the police – whether it be racism-related or raiding the wrong house – was scrutinised by the press and the law.

It was plain odd.

'The other one – you know, the girl the next day – that was his girlfriend; he killed her too. So we have a pattern, Tom. It'll all be wrapped up soon, don't worry.'

It was as if Neil was delivering his conclusions before anyone had been arrested or investigated. Even Thomas knew that wasn't the way to solve a murder.

'So you must have a lot of forensic evidence then? It's watertight, is it?'

Neil waved his hand. 'Don't you worry about that; it's all in hand and taken care of.'

Thomas had wanted to ask what exactly that meant, but his shock prevented him from finding the words.

He also found it strange that Ormond hadn't even used Keira Bradley's name. He understood how the two murders could be seen as different: one woman had stumbled into the path of two crazed thugs on the wrong afternoon, in the wrong park. The other led a life where, unfortunately, you'd expect to run into trouble. However, it was the casual nature of Neil's dismissal of her that riled him. He wasn't about to drive down to the Beacon Estate and make friends with Sharon Bradley, but she'd lost her daughter in the most horrific way, and deserved compassion. And why was Neil so convinced the two murders were linked?

'Revenge. His girlfriend dumped him and he went looking for a woman to hurt – any woman. Then, when she pieced together what he'd done, he killed her too.'

'I thought two people attacked Ella.'

'An accomplice: not hard to get in that area of town.'

'And he's confessed?'

'Not exactly.'

Neil lost his footing at this point and grabbed onto the kitchen counter. Millie was upstairs and Jordan had gone out for a pizza. Thomas's mother was in the bath. He wished she was down here with him to witness the man's curious behaviour. A vase came crashing down onto the tiled floor and smashed into pieces.

Thomas helped him up and he announced that he was leaving.

'You're not driving, are you, Neil?'

'Of course I am.'

'But you…'

'What?'

'You seem unsteady. Surely you've had a bit too much to drink.'

For a moment, Neil stared at him and Thomas felt as though he was going to strike him, or lose his cool in some other way.

'I'm on tablets that might appear to make me look that way, but I have not been drinking.'

That was horseshit. Thomas had smelled it when he helped him up. He wasn't about to get further involved, though, and saw him out, listening to more ranting about lowlifes and what to do with them.

After Neil had gone, he went upstairs and sat for a long time on Ella's side of their bed. They seemed to have become a splintered family of individuals, with their reason to come together gone. They were floating around, and bumping into one another occasionally, awkward, not knowing what to say. Their family had been slashed apart with two knives in Potton Park.

He flicked on the TV to calm his nerves and was assaulted by visions of crowds of people shouting and chanting on the Beacon Estate. They waved banners: *JUSTICE FOR KEIRA! STOP LYING TO US! STOP OUR KIDS DYING!*

Thomas watched with his mouth open. It was like watching something from Beirut in the eighties. Could this be twenty minutes down the pretty road winding along Ullswater's south shore? Surely not? There'd been a mistake. He turned up the volume. It wasn't all yobs either; there were families down there, women and children, there was dancing, singing, speeches and interviews with so-called experts. It was being televised as a whole goddam social movement and his wife was not mentioned once. It was all about the Bradley girl.

Was it all a horrible coincidence? Was Neil trying to pander to him and deliver something counterfeit for the sake of a quick arrest? In his heart, Ella stirred. She agreed.

'Oh Neil, what the hell are you doing?' he said to nobody.

A loud roar went up over the crowd and he watched, transfixed. He went to turn to his wife to tell her about the incredible scenes on their doorstep, but stopped when he realised she wasn't there. He turned back to the TV.

'Dad?'

He looked at the door; it was Millie.

'Darling!' He held open his arms and she came to him. He kissed her head. It was a thing they'd done for as far back as he could remember: she bent her head and he kissed the top of it. She sat on the bed and looked around the room. It broke his heart.

'I'll turn this off,' he said.

'No, I want to watch. It's amazing. Even politicians are waking up and getting involved. We need to stop knife crime. I want to go down there and get Mum on those banners too.'

'What? You can't go down there! I forbid it. It's too dangerous!'

'Dangerous? Jesus, Dad, listen to yourself. Mum got murdered jogging! There are people down there who are making a real difference. They're calling for penal change and social justice. They're demanding rehabilitation of gang members and giving young people a reason to live rather than die.'

'Oh Millie, it's your age. You're altruistic and naïve—'

'Don't you dare!' She stood up and looked at him angrily. He didn't know what to say; he'd never seen his daughter like this. 'Your generation is responsible for what is happening now; you're the naïve ones. You can't shove people into housing estates while you sit in your ivory tower and expect them to behave. You have to look after society as a whole for everyone to feel included.'

'Oh Millie, don't give me that socialist crap. You're too young to understand—'

'God, Dad, I'm ashamed of you. I had no idea you were such a diehard Victorian. I'm sorry that poor people annoy you, because you know that knife crime stats and penal failure stats are mirror images of economic status, right? You really think it's their fault and not circumstances? Shame on you. I don't care for your politics. I'm going to bed.'

'Darling, I'm sorry! There are a thousand and one sides to this and many of them you'll only learn when you become a parent.'

'Good night, Dad. We can talk about it when I'm old enough.' She strode out of the room and he stared at the door.

He heard more doors bang and wished Ella was here. It was the type of conversation he dreaded. He suddenly realised that for the rest of their lives, Jordan and Millie would only have him. Ella wasn't there to be their mentor and guide any more. He was terrified, and he'd already screwed up.

He'd also thrown away a chance to watch TV with his daughter, albeit under unfavourable conditions. Ella had hated the kids spending so much time in their rooms, isolated and on social media, giving in to God knows what influences, and he'd let her down. He felt wretched. Maybe he'd give Millie an hour or so to calm down and then go and apologise. He turned his attention back to the TV.

A smart gentleman with an educated southern accent was being interviewed about youth crime statistics. It caught Thomas's attention because it echoed what his fourteen-year-old daughter had just been scolding him for. The figures were real. The man was a lecturer in criminology at the University of Newcastle. He spoke about how money was ploughed into prisons and yet reoffending rates were alarmingly high: the system was broken. Prison wasn't working. He said that one year in detention for a young male aged between fifteen and seventeen cost the taxpayer over sixty thousand pounds. He argued that the money could be better spent on rehabilitation and community programmes.

Thomas rolled his eyes.

The stats showed not only that the system was expensive, but that inmates were reoffending at a disturbing rate upon release. The professor went on to say that conditions inside prisons were partly to blame and that self-harm rates among prisoners had risen almost one hundred per cent since 2013, while serious assaults on fellow inmates and staff had tripled in five years. The system was haemorrhaging employees and drowning in a sea of incarcerations.

On the screen behind the man, a bunch of youths could be seen by the barricade. As Thomas peered at the image, his blood went cold and he felt his whole body begin to tremble. His breath echoed in his head and the furniture in the room seemed to move around in slow motion as his eyes grew bulging in his head, transfixed on the image.

On the screen, behind the professor, talking to a bunch of youths, dressed as a down and out, he saw his son, Jordan, with the protesters, looking as though he'd been raised there. He shot off the bed and headed to Millie's room to tell her that he had to go out urgently. He crashed through her door and was about to apologise for scaring her when he saw that the room was empty. Her bed was made, her computer and TV off, and her window wide open.

Her room had a pretty ironwork fire escape that led to the ground. He raced down the steps and towards the garage. The door was open, and he saw straight away that Millie's new road bike was missing.

He knew exactly where she'd gone.

Chapter 39

The sun was climbing into the sky. No one in Penrith could see it because it was shrouded in cloud, but it was there, penetrating the dawn and announcing a new day.

Sleeping in makeshift shelters, uncomfortable and cold, most of the overnight dwellers in the growing camp on the Beacon Estate woke early. Dogs milled round looking for food, and stoves were lit ready for tea and coffee. Most of the media people had booked into hotels overnight. The attention that the demonstrations had attracted had prompted editors to sign off budgets for a longer stay: something was brewing and every editor in the country knew it. The powers-that-be could not let this disruption continue indefinitely. It had to come to an end, peacefully or otherwise. Some of the big names in news had begun to arrive the previous evening. They could smell trouble.

Sharon Bradley was the mouthpiece for the movement. Any questions were directed to her, and she made decisions on everything from banner slogans to what to say to the press. What had started out as justice for Keira had become something much bigger and now that Thomas Watson had offered two hundred thousand pounds for information about both murders, it had attracted more attention. Momentum was growing and Sharon walked around like a site manager, checking on volunteers and asking for updates on information given to the police. She had seen for herself the difference between the coppers working for Kelly Porter and the ones who'd acted like twats on Thursday afternoon. Sure, they'd made some arrests and taken some bad boys into custody – some of them had even been charged – but it was Sharon's work with the community that was getting answers.

'You not tired, Shaz?'

'Nah, this is the only thing I wanna do.' It was true: the protests and gatherings had given her a purpose. It was only a matter of time before someone cracked. The Cotton brothers hadn't been seen anywhere on the estate since the release of their photos. Someone must know where they were. DI Porter was on her way here to hear the updates for herself. She was all right, that one, Sharon thought. She could talk to her without feeling as though she was talking to a copper who'd already made up their mind about the victim.

Sharon believed Kelly when she said she was working on both killings equally. She wasn't stupid; she knew that the Watson woman had been rich, beautiful and respectable, while Keira's life had been small and difficult. But they'd both loved, laughed, eaten and slept the same, no matter what anyone said. Millie Watson understood, and that was why she'd turned up here late last night, wanting to meet Sharon.

Her dad had arrived soon afterwards. He was a looker, but shy. Millie had spunk, and Sharon guessed she got it from her mother. Thomas Watson was well dressed and equally nicely mannered. At first he'd wanted to take his daughter straight home, but she'd refused point blank. They'd gone back to Sharon's flat and talked until the small hours, falling asleep as the sun came up. Sharon had put blankets over them and left the house, but now Millie and her dad joined her, and they walked around the camp together.

'You've done all of this, Sharon.' Thomas sounded overwhelmed. 'All I can see is people together, enjoying being connected, singing, planning and working as a team. I've never seen anything like it. What was the estate like before? Did all these people know each other?'

'No. No one ever talked. Everyone was too busy trying to stay away from the Cotton brothers. Now the boot's on the other foot: they're staying away from us!'

'It's truly incredible.'

'We'd like it to be more permanent. It could be so many things: like a centre to bring people together and support each other. There's a lot of problems here.'

'I'm sorry I didn't come sooner.'

'Don't you worry, love, you're here now.' She squeezed his hand.

—

Thomas and Millie were sitting on camping chairs drinking tea. Bacon sandwiches were handed out and they tucked in gratefully.

'No one has mentioned seeing Jordan,' Sharon said. Thomas had explained about seeing him on TV last night and why he knew he'd come here, and his theory about what he was likely up to. He wasn't about to accuse his son of plotting murder, but he knew that was what Jordan wanted. He hadn't come down here to help Sharon, or share his anguish with the community; he'd come to hunt down those responsible. Thomas had to admire his grit, but at the same time, he also knew that it was stupid. Somebody like Jordan, with his privileges and his cosseted life, couldn't possibly hope to dupe two hardened criminals supported by a whole gang of violent thugs.

'I have to find him.'

'Dad, don't leave me,' Millie said.

'Your mother would never forgive me if I lost both of you. And I don't think Jordan will be found unless he wants to be.'

'Will you report him missing?' Sharon asked.

'That could make it worse for him. If he's trying to immerse himself in the world of the gangs around here, which I suspect he is, then putting his face all over the news could be like signing a death warrant.'

'I can't believe he's done this.' Millie was angry with her brother, but also terrified.

Sharon put her arm around her. 'We haven't got enough room for everyone turning up here.' She looked around. 'Some residents have offered their own homes to house a mixture of homeless kids and strays who've come looking for a meal, or just someone who cares.'

'It's astounding, Sharon.' Thomas couldn't praise the woman enough. While he'd been wallowing in self-pity in his mansion by the lake, she had been mobilising people to do something that might make a difference. He felt ashamed.

'Mum would think you're wonderful,' Millie said, and Sharon smiled and patted her hand.

'You know we've got young lads turning up who are gang members?'

'Christ, be careful!' Thomas looked wary.

'I know what you're thinking, but that's the whole point of this. These young kids don't want that life; they want what everyone wants, a place to call home.'

'How do you know they're genuine?'

'I can tell. They're also full of useful information, once they've had a good feed and some love and attention. They feel safe.'

'How do you make them feel safe? The Cotton brothers could be anywhere, taking notes on who's betraying them.'

'There's too many of us now. No one can get through us. Not even them. Today, somebody is gonna walk in here and tell me where they are. I can feel it in my waters. Today is the day.'

Thomas looked at her. Her capacity to hope was extraordinary. All he'd been thinking about was revenge. Smothered in anger and hate, he'd allowed himself to sink to the level of Ella's killers. Jordan had watched him, and might even be carrying out his plans now because of how he'd reacted. This woman was creating something good out of something despicable and showing everybody else the way forward, without a note of self-pity or resentment.

He knew that for the time being, all he wanted to do was stay here, in this place, helping in any way he could.

That, and find his son.

Chapter 40

Kelly arrived at Eden House early. DS Will Phillips was waiting for her. She'd called him last night telling him that she wanted him in the office first thing to clear a few things up. Half of her expected him to go AWOL. But there he was. Emma Hide was at her desk and Kelly greeted them both. Later, she'd take Rob to the Beacon Estate, where they'd get an update from Sharon Bradley and follow up the addresses supplied by Jackson and Tyrone. She'd charged neither with an offence. Before she made any bold moves, she had to find out what Ormond was up to, and why he was so keen for Tyrone to be arrested.

As far as she could work out, from talking to both men and asking crucial questions that only the killers would know, neither Jackson Akers nor Tyrone Fenton was the perpetrator of either killing. The injuries on Tyrone's hand were defensive rather than the result of frenzied stabbing with a slippery blade. Ted had reported evidence of recent sexual activity from Keira's body, but nothing to suggest that it wasn't mutual and consensual. Plus, the clothes at the lab didn't match what Tyrone and Jackson were wearing on the CCTV. Both men, when shown the footage, told exactly the same story about the events of that morning, and despite Kelly playing a few tried-and-tested tricks used on multiple suspects giving evidence about the same event, she hadn't been able to trip them up. The chances of two liars passing that type of test were virtually zero.

Plus, Kelly couldn't ignore the fact that Tyrone Fenton looked truly traumatised and sorrowful over what he'd seen happen to his girlfriend; according to Jackson, he'd been high ever since to numb the pain. She watched both men carefully; she'd been on plenty of body language conferences to spot the basic signs of deceit and earnestness. She believed them. But she had to prove it, and she couldn't help thinking that Jackson was holding something back.

Will followed her to her office and she closed the door. He remained standing.

'I've got something to show you.'

He came around her desk and she tapped a few buttons and brought up the CCTV from B&Q. She let him watch it. He didn't speak, but walked back around the desk.

'I'm all ears, Will.'

'He's an informant.'

'No shit, Sherlock. Since when?'

'I don't know.'

'Bullshit. What have you had out of him?'

'You know I can't share that information, guv. It's intel. He's Liam's, I just go along to provide muscle occasionally.'

'And when his name came up as part of our inquiry, you choose not to tell me because...'

'Same reason. Informants are confidential.'

'So, you and Liam conducted your own interview with him and failed to tell me, even though I'm the SIO on this case and he's a suspect.'

'It was a direct order, ma'am.'

'From?'

'Classified.'

'What? Who the hell are you working for, Will? Because from where I'm sitting, it sure as hell isn't me.'

Will put his hands on top of his head and let out a gasp. He closed his eyes and sat down in the chair opposite Kelly.

'Will, what's going on?'

'I can't... I just can't.'

'Can't what?'

'Before you came here, there were things going on that no one knew about. I don't work in this department. I was brought in when you were, but I work elsewhere.'

'But you've worked for me for three years!'

'No, I haven't.'

Kelly didn't know what to say. Of every scenario she'd run through her head, this was the last one she'd expected. 'You work for Ormond?'

He didn't answer.

'Will, what the hell is he up to?'

'I'm being removed from this role. I leave today. I'm going somewhere else.'

'On whose authority?' She didn't need an answer. 'Why now? This is all linked to the murders, isn't it? It's too neat and tidy. Frame a dodgy lad from the estate and move on. Is that why you and Liam went to see Jackson Akers? To discuss with your informant who to set up? But why would Ormond want an innocent to take the rap? That's what bugging me, Will.'

'I'm sorry, boss, I can't answer any of those questions.'

'Where are you going?'

'I haven't been told.' He got up to leave.

'What's he got on you?'

Will stopped.

'I know you were once a good-for-nothing, weren't you? You and your best mate up to your eyes in trouble. Ormond rehabilitated you; he gave you jobs and saved you from the shit pile.'

Will turned round. His face was screwed with pain, and tears flowed down his face.

Kelly went to him and shook him. 'Jesus, Will! Tell me!'

He pushed her away and left the office.

She stood there for a full minute, not knowing what to make of what she'd seen and heard. Rob and Emma came in.

'Guv, you OK? What happened with Will?'

Kelly sat down, exhausted, frustrated and uncertain.

'I have no idea.'

She stared at her computer and tapped a few keys, finding the phone extension for Liam Brook. She was informed that the officer she sought was off duty until Monday. She told them it was urgent and asked for his address.

She told Rob to get ready for their visit to the Beacon Estate.

'Emma, any luck on that depot?'

'I was going to update you. They have no record of the goods entering the depot but the release form was signed by Ormond.'

'My God, we've got him. We have evidence of the contraband leaving one location and arriving at another, but no record of when it gets there. Come on, Rob. Emma, call me if the lab comes up with anything.'

Chapter 41

Johnny had called Kelly from Penrith to say they'd arrived. He told her that food stalls had been set up at the barricades, and various other vendors and charities were in evidence. Kelly was impressed and keen to see it for herself. Apart from thrusting Keira's case to the forefront of the news, Sharon had also brought the local community together. It was something that made Kelly feel very small. Such simple acts of bravery and commitment were doing more for the Beacon Estate than Ormond ever had.

She couldn't get Will's face out of her head. Whatever Ormond had on him was a bombshell.

She and Rob listened to the radio. It was announced that thousands of people were expected to turn up to Potton Park today to listen to speeches and join a parade to encourage people to come forward with information on the deaths of Ella Watson and Keira Bradley.

'A march for justice has been announced and the crowd will walk peacefully to police headquarters, just outside Penrith. The organisers have assured the press that the action is not designed to aggravate or blame the police. Sharon Bradley, mother of murdered woman Keira

Bradley, told us that she simply wants their voices to be heard. The husband of Ella Watson, who was stabbed in Potton Park, where the demonstration will begin, is marching alongside Sharon, with his daughter.'

'Bloody hell!' Kelly said.

As they neared the park, only a short drive away from Eden House, it became clear that they'd have to dump the car and walk. She flashed her badge at police controlling traffic, and they were directed to a car park that had been emptied for use by squad cars. Kelly looked around her at the huge scale of the operation and felt uneasy. She knew that Johnny would be feeling it too: he'd seen his fair share of crowds turning nasty in the blink of an eye. They were dealing with incendiary emotions, suspects on the run, gang-related crime, and possibly thousands of people. Events like this one always attracted people who loved to stir up trouble, and it didn't take much.

From the car park, it wasn't far on foot to Potton Park, and from there to the Beacon Estate. The streets of Penrith were full of shoppers, normal for a Saturday, and tourists. What wasn't normal was the sound coming across Potton Park from the Beacon Estate. It was like approaching a festival. The joined groups of people heading there and the atmosphere was upbeat. Music played, entertainers did tricks at the side of the road, and burger and candyfloss vans had appeared, making the most of the business opportunity. Kelly and Rob blended in, with their casual Saturday clothes.

They heard a loudhailer.

'I wonder how Thomas Watson got involved, and if Ormond knows what his pal is up to,' she said as they walked.

'I thought they were golf mates?' Johnny asked.

'I know. It doesn't make sense. Unless he wants to get closer to those responsible: like Tyrone's mates. I wonder what he's planning.'

'He could just be here because it's a way to get involved in fighting knife crime.'

'It's odd, though. And to allow his daughter down here.'

'We need to find them; they'll be with Sharon.'

They neared the track that took them from Potton Park to the estate. It was quieter here, because most people were gathering in the park for the march. They made their way to the barricades and were amazed by what they saw.

Lorries and delivery trucks had been allowed access, food stalls had been set up by local retailers, and portable toilets were in place. Several major news channels had erected rainproof shelters, and Sharon sat under one, at a table, giving an interview. Beside her sat Thomas Watson and his daughter, Millie.

Kelly and Rob approached. Sharon waved at them. The interviewer turned around and Kelly asked if they were live. They weren't. The piece was yet to be edited and approved. Reports cobbled together from whatever they had gathered here would be reviewed in one of the huge vans, and the final piece would make the lunchtime news.

'Detective,' Sharon said. Thomas glanced at Kelly; he looked uncomfortable.

'Mr Watson. Millie. I'm surprised to see you down here, but pleased, too. I gather you've been making friends.'

'Dad didn't want to be here. He followed me. I ran away. Jordan is missing. Dad saw him on TV.' Millie didn't mince her words, and Thomas shrugged, as if to reiterate all of the above. He didn't look as though he'd had any sleep.

'What do you mean, Jordan is missing?' Kelly asked.

'He's here somewhere. I saw him on TV last night, he was here and I know he's still here.'

'But you haven't found him?'

Thomas shook his head.

'Dad, he'll be fine, he's doing the same as me.' Millie turned to Kelly. 'I told Dad that to find out what happened to Mum, we need to do what Sharon's doing for Keira: shouting as loud as we can. We've made new banners and everyone knows that we want justice for Keira and Mum.' Kelly looked around and noticed banners with Keira and Ella's names on. It touched her.

'Seems to me like a few ordinary people from a council estate are doing more than you lot,' Sharon said. The journalist stuck his microphone in Kelly's face.

'The investigation is ongoing. These things take time, Sharon, you know that, especially when there are dozens of youths unwilling to help us.'

'Exactly. And do you know why? Because you're fucking useless. You need to take these lads in hand; they think they own the fucking place. This man here has offered two hundred thousand pounds and not one person has come forward with anything useful. It's shameful. You need to be finding those Cotton boys.'

'Actually, that's not true. We have had information, just anonymously.'

The journalist smiled. It was good TV: a bereaved mother giving a copper a toasting with colourful expletives. They'd have to run it past legal first, though, because the police could easily block it.

'How do we get to those lads if no one will tell us where they are?' Kelly asked.

'Raid 'em. Open every friggin' door until you find 'em.'

Millie nodded furiously behind Sharon.

'Head office tried that on Thursday and look what happened. Besides, we're already trying to find the Cotton brothers.'

'Not hard enough.'

Kelly knew why, but she wasn't about to explain to Sharon and Thomas that the man blocking the process and derailing the whole inquiry was her boss.

'You don't think Tyrone did it either, do you? You need to look at your own. No one trusts you.'

'Where did you hear that?' Kelly caught her breath.

Sharon hollered. Kelly winced. A woman came over and Sharon introduced her. She was the mother of a young teenager who'd got involved with the local gang scene. He was scared; he wanted out but didn't know how. He'd been hiding at his auntie's.

'I told her to go and see the solicitor Keira was talking to, but the lad's too scared. Everyone is.'

'Keira was talking to a solicitor?'

'Yeah, someone fancy in Manchester. She got the train there.'

'What about?'

'How would I know? All the letter said was that it was no win no fee or something, and she could get a lot of money. I rang them but they wouldn't talk to me: data protection.'

'Do you have the letter?'

Sharon took a piece of paper out of her jeans and unfolded it. Kelly scanned it, then looked at the woman who'd just arrived.

'Do you think your son would talk to me?'

'No.'

She turned to Sharon.

'Sharon, what you're doing here is incredible. You've got people on the streets, caring for something, fighting for something, and that's amazing. I want to know how you've done it. I want to meet the people helping you. Will you show me what's being done? Who organised the march? What do you intend to do when you get to constabulary HQ?'

'Oh, here we go,' Sharon said. 'This is why she's here. She's been sent by the establishment to put us off.'

'No, you're wrong. I'm on your side.'

'So you're a do-gooder now?'

'I hope that's what I've always been.'

Sharon looked around the tent. Thomas stared at her, exhausted. Millie nodded. A few volunteers shrugged and the journo waited.

'OK then. Let's go.'

'I'll be running a piece on this along the lines of "Local detective reaches out to community",' said the journalist eagerly. 'Can I follow you guys? It's an exclusive.'

'Absolutely.' Kelly needed all the cover she could get in case Ormond made a move. If she became the face of the investigation on national TV, it would be very difficult to get rid of her. The journo looked as though he'd won the lottery.

As the small group left, following Sharon's lead, Kelly waited for Thomas. 'Do you want to file a missing person report for Jordan?' she asked.

'No, I don't think so. He's here. I'm just worried about what his intentions might be.'

'What do you mean?'

'My son is a quiet boy, but don't let that fool you. I've been watching him closely since Ella died, and he's been boiling and simmering deep inside. He's not here to join some community thrust to get justice for his mother.'

They stopped and faced each other.

'He's here for revenge.' Kelly said it for him, and he nodded. 'Right. I hear you. He's running his own investigation.'

'There are several knives missing from the kitchen block.'

'Jesus,' Kelly said. 'You think he's trying to embed himself?'

Thomas nodded and rubbed his eyes; they were red and watery.

'You're exhausted.'

'There's no way I'm leaving the kids. Ella would kill me. I'll stay for as long as it takes.'

'Does Superintendent Ormond know you're here? I hear you and he are golfing pals.'

'And you think that's why he's hell-bent on locking up some poor sod who didn't do it?'

'You read people well.'

'As do you, Detective. Neil was at my house last night when he called you. I thought the way he spoke to you was disgusting. We know each other casually from the golf club; we're not friends.'

Sharon was up ahead, greeting people and checking on how everyone was holding up. It was an incredible sight. She commanded great respect everywhere she went, and groups of people stopped what they were doing and listened to her. This woman who just last week had been virtually housebound was now mobilising a whole community, as well as wider afield, into waking up to the tragedy that was befalling today's youth. It wasn't an exaggeration to say that Sharon Bradley was spearheading something with the potential to bring about real change, and she'd achieved it in less than three days. The hairs stood up on Kelly's arms. She guessed this was how all revolutions began: with a simple message. She hoped fervently that this one succeeded and didn't fizzle out like so many sentiments on TV.

Sharon had stopped and was talking to a man in a suit. She introduced him as a criminologist. The calibre of the visitors attracted by the demonstrations was astounding. Next to him was a woman from a charity representing convicted youths between the ages of fifteen and eighteen: all the teenagers on her files were boys, and all their crimes were gang-related.

Chapter 42

DC Emma Hide entered the main lobby of Eden House and greeted the weekend staff downstairs. During a murder inquiry, the incident rooms upstairs were usually busy at the weekend, but today was different: DI Porter was visiting the barricades on the Beacon Estate, and everybody else on duty except Emma herself was occupied with the hunt for the Cotton brothers. A total of seven addresses had been checked, but the pair remained elusive and it was beginning to look embarrassing for the force.

Emma had felt a mixture of sadness and disappointment when she was told that Will Phillips was leaving the team. She had no idea why, apart from it being personal. She'd worked with Will for three years. He was a decent, ordinary bloke. She'd met Katrina, his wife, when they'd gone out in Penrith to celebrate Will's promotion to DS. It had come on the back of a tough case, as it always did, but Will had never struck her as anything but straight.

Going to London with DI Porter earlier in the year had given her a new insight into her boss. She'd found that she wasn't as hard as her exterior would have people believe. The moment she'd met Matt Carter, the DCI in London in charge of the case, Emma had known that something had gone on between the two of them. She saw it in his eyes and his body language when Kelly was around. He was an old flame for sure.

She liked having a context for the enigmatic Kelly Porter. She had renewed respect for the woman when she saw her as real, like other people, with failed relationships, bad choices in men, a vulnerable heart and a complicated past. When she found out exactly why Kelly had left London, it had added sympathy to the growing list of emotions she felt towards her boss. Publicly, the Met claimed that sexism, misogyny, favours and favourites were a thing of the past, but everyone knew that was bollocks. As long as women had wombs – despite new targets for promotion – they'd stay on the back foot. Real status was won on the street.

The Coryn Boulder murder case had been a fuck-up from the start. Carter had been in charge; not in name – Kelly Porter was equal in rank – but for the purposes of those in the know, because his uncle was a superintendent. He had cut corners that Porter never even knew about. When the suspect in the case committed suicide by jumping off a multistorey car park, the finger was pointed at Kelly. But it was Carter who'd suppressed the information from a witness that Coryn's boyfriend was seen dumping black bags in the bins behind her flat a day after her death. The information was ignored because they were so close to nailing the other suspect.

In the event, Porter was thrown under the bus. Carter claimed she was the one who'd handled the witness statements. The inquiry was internal – not deemed serious enough to involve third parties – and put in a drawer. Carter was promoted. Porter was told the 'mistake' would be overlooked if she agreed to look at other constabularies.

A good Cumbrian granny might say that she'd been stitched up like a kipper.

Emma returned her attention to her current inquiries. She'd called the lab and they'd told her that they would have news for her around ten o'clock. It was Kate Umshaw's day off. The office buzzed with a low hum and she was glad that she was able to concentrate on her screen in peace.

She heard a noise and looked behind her. Kelly's door was open, so she got up to close it. Will was sitting at the boss's desk.

There was a moment between them where Emma didn't know what to say and Will simply looked at her. Time stood still.

'The boss said you're leaving. Is that true?'

'Yes, I'm being moved.'

'Why?'

'Don't you start!' He was short with her and it took her by surprise. He sighed. 'I'm sorry. I was getting some information on Jackson Akers and Tyrone Fenton. I just…'

He was nervous. Emma thought it was because he'd been caught doing something he shouldn't.

'If you're leaving the team, why do you need information about the case?'

'You're right. Old habits.' He got up and walked past her.

'Will?'

He ignored her and left.

Emma rang her boss, but her call went unanswered. She went back into DI Porter's office and logged onto her computer. The first thing she did was check recent activity. Will wasn't a fool; whatever he'd been doing, he could easily erase the record. He was a nerd like her. But she knew ways around all the tricks.

It didn't take long to unpick what he'd done.

He'd been looking at DI Porter's recent searches. One was his own career profile and the other was Ormond's.

More worryingly, there had been a recent download of data to a removable USB stick. It left DI Porter wide open.

Her mobile phone made her jump and she answered. It was the lab.

Neither of the knives retrieved from the lake in Potton Park matched Tyrone Fenton's prints. They'd had positive results, though, from the Police National Computer database. The prints on the smaller blade belonged to Adam Cotton, and they also had a match for the larger blade: a known accomplice of the Cotton brothers. The clothes supplied by Jackson Akers last night had been tested urgently, and three chestnut hairs had been found with the same follicle profile as one found on Keira Bradley. Emma knew from his photograph that Jason Cotton had chestnut hair. The sweater had tested positive for Keira's blood, and the small knife had a single usable print that matched to none other than Jason Cotton. If neither brother had had a police record, it could have taken months, if not years, to find matches. The past had a nasty habit of catching up.

The semen found inside Keira tested positive for Tyrone Fenton, but they'd expected that. The clothes taken from the raid on Tyrone's flat yielded no physical evidence of a violent event. They found a hair matching Keira's follicle profile and skin cells matching her DNA, but the pair were lovers, so again, no surprise.

She tried Porter once more. This time she answered. Emma told her the lab results first.

'That is fantastic news. Bloody brilliant! Listen, I need you to get on to the counter-corruption intelligence unit to find out how to whistle-blow.'

'Whistle-blow?'

'I don't believe the reporting of such a senior officer would be handled sensitively enough unless I'm anony-mous.'

'Good point. It should be on their website.'

'And there's a solicitor in Manchester I want you to call to see if we can get Keira's file.'

'She was seeing a solicitor?'

'Yes. I want to know why. You'll have to get a police production order.'

'Guv, Will was in your office, on your computer, looking at your recent searches.' She didn't know how else to say it, so she just blurted it out.

'What? Shit.'

Chapter 43

Neil Ormond teed off the tenth and felt the stretch in his spine. He planned to play the back nine.

His mobile phone vibrated in his pocket and it irritated him. The swing was good, and followed the correct line, but the wind gusted at the wrong moment and took it fifty yards to the left, into a tree.

Damn!

He looked at the caller and knew he had to take it. It could be the information he was seeking. He'd been requesting intel on DI Kelly Porter for months, and had slowly been gathering material on her. She was simply too good. He couldn't be seen to stand out, and Porter was attracting attention from HQ for her outstanding detective work. She'd put away more criminals in the last three years than the rest of the serious crime department over the previous decade. It made him look incompetent. If she could waltz in here and flip the stats on their heads, then what had the rest of them been doing before?

The caller was his best contact in the Met. He was solid, reliable and prompt. He'd been a rookie under Ormond many moons ago and they kept each other up to date about any anomalies that might pop up in day-to-day policing.

'Yes,' he said loudly into his phone, as if the increased volume would bring welcome news. The knot in his stomach, however, told him otherwise.

'There's been some digging around the employment files of two of your boys.'

Ormond waited.

'The searches came from a fixed computer station at Eden House. This morning, one of them confirmed they were done from the computer of DI Porter. There've also been questions asked at the Preston depot by a DC Emma Hide. In addition, a police production order has been requested to acquire a file at a solicitor's in Manchester regarding Keira Bradley. It has been granted.'

Neil ended the call. He slammed his driver into his new Ping golf bag, and set the caddy to auto. It set off like R2-D2 and trundled alongside him towards where he thought he'd fucked up his shot. He fiddled with his glove and looked up to the sky, as if the heavens might provide an answer as to why a junior upstart might be checking on his business. She was even better than he'd thought.

He was ashamed of his behaviour last night, but only because it had probably alienated Tom. He'd made a fool of himself. He should have got Porter on board when she first came to Cumbria, but he knew that was an impossibility due to her incorruptible damn morals. That was why he'd planted Will: to keep an eye on her. But the young officer had grown soft and warmed to his new boss. He could see it and it was time to do something about it.

For anything to come back to him, she had to prove it. But he had no idea how to get around the Manchester solicitor; that was impossible even for him. They were independent legal experts and untouchable. Sometimes

277

Neil couldn't figure out how he'd got embroiled in all of this. It was days like today when he wanted to collect his passport from home and disappear to some remote village on a foreign island in the sun.

The frustration welled up inside him and threatened to bubble over into anger. He saw two groups of old-timers, and they waved from the ninth fairway. He'd been invited to join them but had declined. Sometimes he just needed to be alone and concentrate on his strokes. Today was one of those days, but now it'd been spoiled. Greed. It ruined everything eventually. He'd been too greedy, but he searched around for something else to blame.

Female police officers. They were a nightmare: into everything, desperate to prove themselves worthy, as if making up for not having a dick. They'd ruined the force. He harked back to the days when men sat in boardrooms thick with cigarette and cigar smoke, making decisions and plans, only interrupted by the odd skirt bringing them tea or brandy. He shook his head: how times had changed. Now everything was transparent and it was frankly dull.

Conditions were becoming tighter and tighter. Every-thing was documented, checked and accounted for. Leakage was a thing of the past. Well, almost. He needed to get out of the gig, he knew that much, and he wondered if he could hold on until retirement.

He calmed a little and remembered when he'd first met Colin Day. In those days, coppers weren't either straight or bent; they used their intuition. Sometimes people got hurt and sometimes contraband went missing. It all added to the flavour. One thing was for sure: they formed bonds with the crims and it garnered results. Nowadays, with instinct dead in a sterile textbook somewhere, hawked over by lawyers and journos, coppers daren't even take a piss without logging it on a time sheet.

His stint with Merseyside Police had shaped him in many ways. They'd dealt with some of the worst criminals in recent British history. People thought gangs were a modern phenomenon. They knew very little. In Liverpool, in the seventies, without mobile phones, computers or the Internet, gangs ruled the streets with impunity. It was brutal. He'd cut his teeth pursuing people like the Cotton brothers, until he saw – plain as day – that he was banging his head against a brick wall. As with anything in life, it was good to talk, and talking to crims was no different. An agreement; that was what was needed. And that was what was needed now, on the Beacon Estate. But Kelly Porter was on a mission to turn the whole place upside down. Righteous, self-assured pussy was going to be his downfall.

Tombday had been a code word made up by Colin Day and covering a huge operation, beginning with betting and tanning shops in Workington and Liverpool, and ending in recruiting traffickers from Sarajevo. It was only a matter of time until they got caught: they'd simply become too big. But it was Kelly Porter who'd dug them out, like a terrier after a fox: she hadn't let up until she had the lot of them behind bars, or so she thought. And now he remembered where he'd heard the name Emma Hide before. She was so cosy with Porter, she might as well be up her backside. The young detective had been Porter's sidekick in London earlier in the year. It made sense: she was a computer whizz. A bright spark in Kelly's team.

He needed to think clearly, and whistled as he followed his automated caddy. He corrected its trajectory, but for the most part it sensed where he was and adjusted itself. It had cost the best part of a thousand pounds, but it was his treat. Much of the money laundered by Tombday had needed someone to look after it. He reached the treeline and looked for his ball. It was a matter of principle. He could easily have got out a brand-new one and dropped it on the fairway, but he'd only berate himself for it for the rest of the day. He had to find it. Eventually he spotted it, in deep grass underneath a silver birch. He commanded the caddy to halt and decided to play a wedge to get out of the rough.

On the next hole, he realised that it was no use. These damn women had messed up his swing. He couldn't get his shoulders to relax and the ball kept pinging this way and that. He hit trees, he couldn't pitch, and he chose the wrong irons. He set the trolley to auto and made his way sulkily back to the clubhouse.

He left his kit outside and changed his shoes, then went into the bar area to grab some lunch. Once his belly was full, he'd make a decision on what to do next. DI Porter and her team were dealing with some pretty nasty criminals right now, and it was part of the risk of the job that one occasionally crossed paths with peril.

The huge TV in the bar was up loud and the tables were busy. He greeted old pals but couldn't help but be drawn to the screen. The bulletin was live from the Beacon Estate, and he watched in shock as the scenes unfolded. There were thousands of people there, marching, singing, chanting, waving banners and demanding social reform. He couldn't believe what he was seeing. Politicians, experts and celebrities were all giving opinions and bemoaning inequality.

He was about to roll his eyes and order a beer when the image on the screen switched to an interview with Sharon Bradley, who was appealing for information regarding the death of her daughter. Sitting next to her, nodding her head like a lapdog, was Millie Watson, holding a banner that read *JUSTICE FOR ELLA AND KEIRA*.

Dear God.

But it was the background that caught his attention: DI Kelly Porter, deep in conversation with Thomas Watson.

He walked out of the club without ordering his drink.

Chapter 44

Adam Cotton was playing FIFA on an old Xbox 360.

He and his brother had been lying low in a warehouse just north of the Beacon Estate, staying out of trouble while the police sorted out the mess. Only a select few knew where they were. The room at the top of the warehouse was furnished with sofas, tables and chairs, a fridge, and a small TV set connected to the Xbox. No one had any interest in watching events unfold on the Beacon Estate; their only concern was staying away from the heat. Jason had a widespread network of garages, flats and warehouses across Penrith, but relied on others to make sure plans were executed, and goods received and sold on time and to the right person. He didn't trust Adam with that side of the business; he was merely a hired thug.

The game was tense, with Adam just losing out on a sitter. He punched the boy next to him and threw the console towards the screen. Then he got up and kicked a chair, which flew across the concrete floor.

'Calm down, bro. You're proper shit at that game, man. For real. What is the point of you throwing your toys around?' Jason admonished from his seat in the corner, where he was smoking a hand-rolled cigarette and contemplating his future. He shook his head. He'd lost all respect for his brother. It had been a long time coming, but now he saw him merely as baggage. He had to cut loose, and he needed quiet to get his thoughts straight. Adam was fucking up his head space.

'Shut up, brah!' Adam spread his hands and confronted him; they were all growing jumpy. Being holed up together, not able to go out, had given them a serious case of cabin fever.

Jason laughed at him. Adam looked around and noticed that others were smirking along. He lunged at one boy, but he was too slow and the boy moved in time, escaping towards the door.

'Where do you think you're off to?' Adam shouted.

'Fuck you, brah. I'm going out.'

Adam went to follow him.

'Leave it!' Jason barked the order and Adam stopped, turning back. Anger burned into his dark skin, though it was difficult to tell where the bruises ended and the high colour started. The brothers stared at one another and the others in the room thought there might be another fight, a more even one. Last time, Adam had been proper stoned and didn't stand a chance. He seemed more with it now, and he was fuelled by humiliation.

'Fuck him, brah, you can't go out, you know that. It only takes one sighting and we're all fucked.'

Jason had given Adam a reason not to bite, and it was a sensible and respectable one. It restored some of his pride. The dynamic inside the warehouse had shifted and Jason saw that now: those not identified by the police had no reason to stay there, and the Cotton brothers had become too reliant upon them. Leaving the building was a defiant act, and it wouldn't take long for others to follow, either from sheer boredom, or, more sinisterly, because they recognised their new power.

Either way, the brothers had to get out.

Adam used to be alert, funny and strong. Now, when Jason looked at him, all he could see was a withered body and a wasted mind. Chemicals of all kinds, snorted, smoked, injected, rubbed, inhaled and consumed, had conspired to ravage a young body to a state where he was beyond salvage. And he'd done it to himself. That was why the posh woman was dead: because Adam had been snorting ketamine. The two stabbings were supposed to take place around the same time – one to cover the other – but Adam, bolstered by chemicals, had got ahead of himself.

Jason had grown up around hard drugs and dealt them from the age of eleven, but he'd never quite got on with them. He opted for clarity. Drugs sullied his mind, and he knew that control was impossible when the brain started to bend. Sure, he had fun – when it was safe – but he knew his limits and wanted to live beyond thirty. In a warped kind of way, he admired Guns Akers, but he'd never let on. Guns never lost control, and out of everyone, he was the surest candidate for surviving. And he had the bag. Tyrone had confessed that, instead of destroying the gear, or storing it somewhere safe, he'd panicked and given it to his best friend. Jason should have known that Tyrone would go running to Guns after he'd squealed like a baby as he watched his bitch die. He was furious with himself for losing control, but he couldn't help it; sticking the blade in had felt so good. But it also meant that his clothes had been covered in blood. The knife had become sticky and he'd only stopped thrusting when he'd lost his grip and cut himself.

He stubbed out his cigarette and stood up. 'I'm going for some air.' Something about being in the same room as his brother and the goonies who surrounded him made him claustrophobic.

He stuck to the landing in the hallway, just to get some space; he knew he could go no further. If he could convince Guns to work with him and set Adam up, they could walk away with two hundred K and disappear. The rig in Cumbria was over for now, but there'd be others. Jason had good contacts all over the country; maybe he could start afresh in Europe. Paris was fast becoming the new centre of illicit trade in substances, and everyone spoke English.

But first, he wanted to talk to the bent copper. They used burner phones, one-time-use mobile devices that were disposed of after each transaction, to avoid being traced. Some geek on the other side of the world might be able to track the phone via satellite, but never the purchaser. Even the mobile virtual network operator could provide data from a one-off use mobile such as Jason used all the time, but he never gave a name when purchasing one, so it was foolproof if you stuck to the plan and discarded the gadget after every contact. They were cheap, reliable and utterly untraceable to a human being. Adam was sloppy with his and kept them for longer than he should. It would be easy to trace him to this warehouse if Jason could get a message to somebody. He was owed that much. He'd done what was asked of him; how the hell was he expected to know that the woman who was jogging through Potton Park when his brother was tripping off his tits on ket would turn out to be pals with the gaffer? No one, that was who.

He took a burner phone from his pocket and dialled the number recently given to him: they changed frequently. It was answered quickly and the exchange was short. A meeting place was arranged.

He'd go alone.

Chapter 45

Kelly waved at Johnny. They'd found each other in Potton Park, after a few phone calls. She wanted to check in with them all. She was acutely aware that these things could easily turn ugly. Callum and Josie were chomping on burgers, and the smell of cooking fat and burnt sugar filled the air. It was like a fair.

They watched as hundreds of people of all ages gathered in preparation for the speeches and the proposed march to police HQ. Kelly wondered if it would actually go ahead. Sometimes events like this talked the talk but fell flat. Ted treated everybody to hot chocolate and they hugged the plastic cups to warm their hands. Kelly still had a lot to do, but seeing her family was a welcome diversion, even if it was a short one. Rob had come with her, and was chatting to Johnny about security and potential flash points around the park. They nodded and gestured, and Kelly wondered why Johnny hadn't joined the force after he left the army. She knew the answer, though: he'd had enough of watching people do awful things to one another.

Sharon, Thomas and Millie were at the front of the crowd, on a hastily erected stage, where somebody had set up a PA system. Sharon was due to give a speech before the march set off; Kelly wanted to hear it but suspected she wouldn't have time. The crowd stilled and a man took the microphone and greeted the crowd, then introduced Sharon.

Kelly looked around and didn't see any cause for concern. Except for the piles of litter, water bottles and other detritus from a large human gathering, there seemed to have been no problems. But that could change as they got on the move. She wouldn't follow the march: that was a job for the transport and tactical police. But Callum and Josie were desperate to get involved. Johnny looked at Kelly; she knew that inside he was squirming.

'Look, if you're with them, what can happen?' she said.

'Please, Dad! We could have sneaked here anyway without telling you.'

'She's got a point,' Ted said. As always, he stuck up for Josie.

Callum chipped in. 'Come on, when do we ever get an opportunity to be involved in something like this? The TV cameras are everywhere, it'll be talked about for years, and when your grandchildren ask you where you were when the people marched from Potton Park, what will you say?' His question was directed towards Johnny, and everyone looked at him, waiting for his answer. It was a bold address, and Josie squeezed Callum's arm. The tussle was over and the teenagers had won.

'Call me!' Kelly made them promise to keep in touch.

They said their goodbyes and Kelly and Rob made their way back to the estate. As they approached the flats, they heard Sharon's voice over the mic in the distance. There was still a police presence, but the barricades were like ghost towns compared to an hour earlier. The press had accompanied the walkers and left only a skeleton presence behind with those unable to join in. The elderly, infirm or those otherwise incapacitated had stayed behind to cook, tidy up and make more banners in preparation for the return of the protesters. There was no plan to pack up and go home: this was just the beginning.

It was a weird sensation entering streets where previously there had been throngs of people giving interviews, singing, dancing, and shouting through loudhailers. Now there was quiet and an eerie sense of desertion.

It was an opportunity for Kelly to call the solicitor in Manchester. She'd been sent the production order by email. She paced up and down near the main barricade outside Wordsworth Towers and waited to be connected.

Rob stamped his feet to keep warm and watched his boss make the call. When she'd finished, she turned to him, and he was shocked at the expression on her face.

'I need to call the counter-corruption intelligence unit.'

'Boss?'

'Keira identified Ormond as part of a network that supplied underage girls to older men. It was part of Tombday, do you remember? They took girls to parties, got them stoned or drunk, and raped them. Keira was part of that for a while, until Sharon put a stop to it. Keira recognised Ormond on TV and found this solicitor online. She never told Sharon what she was doing.'

'Jesus. And you reckon Ormond found out?'

'And had her taken out. But to make it look like a spate of gang attacks, he ordered a second, random hit.'

'But they fucked up.'

They walked towards Wordsworth Towers. Ordinarily, she would call something like this in; her whole team would be in position, ready to follow the same trajectory as the boss. It wasn't so now. She still didn't know whose side Will was on, or Liam Brook. Her head screamed that Will had been doing Ormond's dirty work all along, but her heart wouldn't allow it. For Will to be a party to this made a mockery of everything she'd ever thought or felt about him. She couldn't deal with that now.

'We need to get Jackson and Tyrone somewhere safe,' she said.

Rob agreed. 'I'm with you, boss.'

They approached Jackson's floor and made their way along the balcony. Kelly knocked on the door and spoke quietly.

'Jackson, it's Kelly Porter.'

The door opened. Part of her was surprised to see him; the other part was fearful that he'd double-crossed her. He always seemed to be where he should be.

'Are you alone?'

'Yeah. I was just about to leave.'

'Where are you going? Were you hoping to run away?'

Jackson stood back and let them in. He looked guilty, and Kelly knew she was correct.

He nodded. 'I expected you'd turn up here, so I left a present for you in the living room.' They followed him in.

'A present?'

They went into the room and saw boxes and bags on the floor.

'Evidence I've looked after for the Cotton brothers. It's all yours; I'm out of here.'

Rob blocked his way.

'Jackson. I need your help. I'm on my own here. Rob has my back, but my boss – the guy behind all this – wants me out of the way. I'm putting everything on the line too.'

'You've already had my help. If it wasn't for me, you'd never have known what happened.'

'I know, and that's why you have to stay. Run away now and you'll be caught. Or what's the alternative? A life on the run? It would kill you. Don't change your mind now.'

'She's right,' Rob said.

'Keira had gone to a solicitor about something a very senior police officer was involved in. I think that's why she was killed. She said he molested her, seven years ago, at a party held somewhere in the Lakes for older men seeking underage girls, some as young as ten. They were picked up off the streets, shipped in, drugged and used for sex. She recognised him from a newspaper when he posed for a charity event. It wasn't an isolated case; there were hundreds of these parties over the years, and Keira was close to exposing his part in them.'

Jackson sat down heavily on the sofa. 'I knew Sharon back then. I'd run away from a home, and she took me in. Keira had disappeared, and she was worried sick. When she came back, she had this look in her eyes, and she wasn't right after that.'

'Jackson, what is happening here is unprecedented. Stay and help Sharon Bradley rebuild this place. This is your opportunity to give something back.'

He laughed.

'I know you think it's bullshit, but I can see it behind your eyes: you believe in people. You're in a position to make a difference. How does that feel? Has it ever happened before? Are you scared of it?'

'Fuck's sake, man! Leave me alone!' He put his head in his hands. Kelly knelt in front of him and took his hands in hers. He looked up at her.

'I'm going to be with you every step of the way. This is about looking forward, not back. It's only a matter of time before we get the Cotton brothers, and we've got the evidence we need.'

'But… I did stuff.'

'Did you hurt anyone?'

He shook his head.

'You were a courier?'

He nodded.

'Couriers get less than three years these days, unless you're dealing as well, and that should be commuted for your testimony.'

'You can't guarantee that.'

'There are no guarantees for anything. Where's Tyrone? We need to get you both out of here.'

A door opened, and Tyrone appeared.

Chapter 46

Jordan Watson bought a pasty from one of the corner shops that dotted the Beacon Estate. There weren't as many as there used to be, not since the Tesco Metro had opened near the main tower block, close to the back entrance to the estate. Jordan was getting to know the layout pretty well.

He followed the crowd, not in a rush to go anywhere in particular, just gathering intelligence on how the estate worked. He knew, like everyone knew, that the police were after the Cotton brothers. He also knew that he had to find them first.

He had their faces burned into his memory. The last time he'd seen them was in the flat where drill music hurt his head and bodies came and went in a heaving mass, on the lookout for drugs or just to hang out somewhere illicit.

He flitted between intense concentration – formulating a plan – and simply watching, fascinated by how so loose a network could maintain a stranglehold on so many young people. It was the implementation of fear politics at its finest: he'd studied it in history lessons, analysing some of the most brutal regimes the world had ever seen, and it was alive and well inside this casual yet lethal band of brothers. On one level it was laughable – the lack of solid structure – but that was the point: structure killed regimes from the inside. Disorganisation was key when keeping human beings in a state of constant limbo and terror.

He knew from stories retold with vigour, for entertainment, by the boys and men he'd hooked up with, that the Cotton brothers earned every ounce of kudos they held, and wouldn't hesitate to stick a blade into any person brave or stupid enough to challenge them. Jason was apparently the brains and Adam the incendiary device. Both vital, both necessary.

After his run-in with Adam, he'd dismissed him as a meathead. A dangerous meathead but one nonetheless. And he looked like a regular junkie. Jordan reckoned that Adam would be the easier of the two to overpower, if he had surprise on his side, and found him alone. The brothers were hiding somewhere, everyone knew that. There couldn't be many people with him, and as the noose tightened, they'd start leaving.

Jason was a different beast. He was the one who called the shots. But Jordan reckoned Adam had gone out on a limb where his mother was concerned. Everyone knew that if a random hit on a woman had been ordered, it would be Jason who'd do it. Adam was the loose cannon, and it hadn't gone unnoticed that he was nursing some pretty serious wounds: to his ego and to his face. Word had it that his brother had taught him a lesson for going rogue.

The people Jordan had met assumed him to be driven by scoring drugs, finding girls and riding bikes, but Jordan had been listening to every word. If he stopped for too long and thought of anything else, he reckoned he would go mad. The realisation that his mother might have been butchered on a whim was too much. He busied his mind with the girl he'd slept with, feeling disappointed with himself. He'd imagined chasing a girl for weeks, even months, before she allowed him to go that far. Here on the estate, within hours, he'd found someone who'd done it straight away. They'd performed the most intimate act together, and afterwards had nothing to talk about.

He guessed she was used to it by the way she got dressed afterwards and giggled at him. Her hands had been expert, as was her body, though she could be no older than sixteen. That level of experience came with multiple encounters, surely, and he began to worry about STDs. He'd seen disgusting photos online of rotting penises and wart-riddled vaginas. They hadn't used a condom; she hadn't given him time. He heard his mother in his head and remembered their conversations about condoms.

'It's less about pregnancy than about disease. It only takes one infected person to have sex with ten women and that's it: game over. Think about that.'

He'd thought her over the top, but now, not so much. His cheeks burned and he bit into his pasty hard to try to erase her voice from inside his head. He had work to do and she was distracting him.

The group began to disperse, and he tagged along with a splinter group of boys who looked pretty streetwise. Their language was ingrained in the way they moved their bodies, and it was as if Jordan was watching a role play. They were tight. Not so tight that they would shut him out: why would they do that? The potential of a new member was always welcome, and waifs and strays were the mainstay of what they did, but at some point he'd have to prove himself of value.

'That bitch is moving mad, rah. She's bare jarring, say nuffin'.'

Jordan translated the hotchpotch of gang words quickly; he'd been exposed to them for a long time. He worked out that he'd just been told that the girl he'd had sex with yesterday, in front of a room full of other grinding blood, was somewhat promiscuous, as well as crazy. He couldn't agree more.

'Time to move on, blood. I need a trek.' He communicated that he was friendly and he fancied a walk.

They fist bumped. 'Safe.'

'Come wiv, blood. My yard is a bare trek away. I got some sweet one for us right there. Still.'

The young man who'd spoken indicated a group of girls, and made his intention clear that he was about to invite them all over to his place to take drugs. It was a positive step and might take him closer to his target. Jordan wasn't sure what gave him the vibe about this particular group, but they smacked of confidence, control and swagger: perfect traits for the hard core of any gang. He could feel himself growing closer and closer to Jason and Adam Cotton. Someone, somewhere knew where they were, and young lads taking drugs had loose mouths.

In hiding, the brothers would need help. They wouldn't be able to remain immune to the heat radiating towards them for long, unless they had a secure network of loyal aides. By now, everyone in the county, if they hadn't had their heads up their arses, knew their names, and his dad's two hundred K was up for grabs.

He shuffled along with them and the girls tagged behind. They wore their hoods up and Jordan fastened a bandanna around his mouth when he'd finished eating, throwing his pasty wrapper to the floor. Delinquency, he decided, felt rather satisfying.

An unwelcome image of his sister's face appeared in his head and it made him angry. Why now, he had no idea, and he closed his eyes, willing her to go away. He had to stay steely if he was to have any chance of ending this.

He became aware of a car slowing behind them, and the two alpha males of the group stopped. They held their hands up in a reassuring gesture and nodded, before approaching the vehicle. The others slowed, but kept walking. Jordan looked behind him. The two men were talking to the driver, who looked to be in his thirties, and fairly respectable.

Jordan covered his face and looked away. He knew the driver. The men were spreading their hands and shaking their heads. It was clear that it was an uncomfortable conversation, but there was some type of understanding between them. They knew each other. He watched as the man handed something over and it was put swiftly into a coat pocket. The whole time, the boys never revealed their faces. The driver shot a glance in Jordan's direction and his heart almost stopped. He quickly told himself that no one would ever recognise him in this ridiculous get-up: he looked like all of them.

When the two rejoined the group, they said nothing of their encounter. Jordan mulled it over. He'd seen plenty of examples of the police talking to people on the estate over the last twenty-four hours. They had varied from cartoonish – in the sense that the coppers looked way out of their depth and were ridiculed into moving on – to raw hatred. This encounter had been neither. It wasn't a fact-finding exercise, and it wasn't a casual interview by a copper doing the rounds. Neither had it been menacing. It had been more of a friendly chat and an exchange of goods.

Chapter 47

Will drove away, with Liam next to him. For three hundred quid, they now had the address of a warehouse in Penrith where the Cotton brothers were hiding, no doubt unaware of the amount of evidence being gathered against them. They'd be thinking to ride out the storm until Tyrone Fenton was arrested and charged for the murders and they could all go back to normal.

There was no normal any more.

He'd watched, helpless, as Kelly had worked her way deeper and deeper to the core of what was really going on. Maybe she'd put the last few puzzle pieces together already.

'Should we call it in?' Liam asked.

'No, first we go to Ormond.'

'What, to his house?'

'Where else? Let's go and see how far his loyalty extends when his skin is on the line instead of ours.'

'What do you mean?'

Will looked at his long-time friend. He didn't need to say anything. The two of them understood one another without saying a word.

They drove in silence. Ormond lived outside Penrith on some swanky new-build estate. They'd never been invited there, and had never had a reason to go, until now. They'd supposed that it would always come to this one day, and now that day had arrived. It was only mid-afternoon, but the sky was grey and the surrounding fields were covered in a thin layer of snow, merging the colours into one drab canvas. The big dump hadn't happened, mainly because it was too cold.

They were glad in a way not to be working. Work came with a set of uncertainties that they faced almost weekly. There was always something to do for Ormond. It had never crossed their minds to say no.

Liam looked out of the window and Will concentrated. The traffic was light and they soon neared the address. Will's heartbeat was slow and calm; he hadn't felt such liberation for years. Not since the night he'd met Liam.

It had been freezing cold, he remembered that much. The radiators in the children's home were old and useless, and anyway, the bastards who ran the place kept them off to save money. Will was crying in his bed, trying to get warm under a blanket. A blanket stained with his blood. Liam sat on the bed and asked him if he wanted to read a book together under the blanket, using a tiny torch he had.

He'd stopped crying. They soon became warm and fell asleep reading the book. From that night, they were inseparable. They shared moments of laughter together, and even some joyous times in the home. They also shared the horrors together, and both believed that it was the other who kept them alive. Ormond had thrown them a lifeline, but he also knew their secrets.

The house was grand, and a Mercedes was parked in the driveway.

They went past it and parked on the street. Still they didn't speak. They'd become so adept at understanding what the other was thinking and feeling, that colleagues sometimes found it odd working with them.

That wasn't their concern.

They went to the back of the house and peered carefully in through the windows, hoping to find Ormond at home. If not, they'd break in anyway and wait for him. He was in there, walking to and from a room off the kitchen, carrying papers and boxes, packing files into a suitcase. Will and Liam exchanged glances and nodded. They knew that if he was packing files away, he must know the game was almost up, and that he needed to tidy up what he could. That also meant that he was very unlikely to answer the door. So they rapped on the patio doors off the kitchen.

Ormond froze, but relaxed when he saw who it was. The relief soon turned to anger at the audacity of them turning up to his private address. He opened the door.

'What do you two want? How dare you come to my house! My wife could have been here.'

Liam and Will looked at one another: it was confirmation that they were alone.

'Sir, we didn't know what else to do. Porter knows everything. She's spoken to the solicitor Keira was seeing, and she's got solid forensics against the Cotton brothers for both murders.'

'How solid?'

'Concrete.'

'What about the plant?' His voice was becoming loud and his face was turning red.

'It never happened. We reckon one of the informants turned and is now working with Porter.'

'Have you taken care of him?'

'We can't find him, sir.' Though Will used the formal title, he spoke through gritted teeth. Ormond didn't notice.

'Porter has to be taken out.'

'Sir?'

Ormond looked at the two men and smiled. 'This is all going to be fine as long as she is taken care of. Come on, lads, are we getting cold feet? You have to do it; you know what will happen if you don't.'

'She's a respected officer, sir.' Will appealed to reason, but he could feel the situation slipping from his grip.

'I can change that. I can prove her incompetence and arrogance. No one will miss her.'

'Sir, we know where the Cotton brothers are. Why can't we cut ties to them and let the law do its job? They go down, as they deserve, and we come up with a plan.'

'A plan? For what? It's there in black and white in that solicitor's office. You fucked up!' Ormond was roaring now, and pointing at them.

'Sir...' Will tried to prolong the discussion. Liam was clenching and unclenching his fists. Will couldn't believe that they were being blamed for what Ormond had done. It was clear that no matter what they said, he was cutting himself loose.

'I don't need you two cowboys coming here and suggesting plans! Get out of my sight! And if you think of squealing when I'm gone, remember I still have the video tape. I swear on my mother's life that every newspaper in the country will get that film.'

Before Will could stop him, Liam had walked to the kitchen counter and grabbed a knife from a block. He advanced on Ormond, who backed away around the island in the centre of the room. Chaos erupted. Will felt as though he was moving in slow motion, begging Liam not to be stupid. Ormond was old and slow and he tripped over a stool.

Liam got to him first and lifted the blade, staring into Ormond's terrified eyes. Then he brought it down. Ormond screamed over and over again, but as the blows rained down, he stopped making any sound at all.

Will couldn't watch, and turned away, only looking back when the noise of flesh being ripped apart subsided and Liam sat panting on Ormond's chest. He was covered in blood.

Will went to him and shook him.

'Get up.'

Liam did what he was told. Will took the knife and threw it in the sink.

'We have to tidy up. Get those clothes off.'

Liam came back to the present and stared at him. Then he nodded and started to undress. Will found black bags under the kitchen counter and shoved everything into one. Then he checked the ground floor and found a shower, directing Liam to it, making sure he left no bloody prints.

'Get yourself clean.'

While Liam was showering, Will found cleaning prod-ucts and a bucket and set about mopping up what he could and cleaning anything he could remember touching. With Ormond dead, they might just get away with this, he thought. But then reason kicked in and he knew that was an impossibility, though when the counter-corruption unit found out what the man had been up to, they'd realise that any number of people could have a motive to kill him.

A shadow crossed his mind and he realised that he'd never find the tape now, not without ripping the house apart.

He checked that Liam's things were all in the bag, and that everything was clean. They could do nothing about the body. Moving it would leave too much transferrable evidence: he'd worked as a detective for long enough to know that. It was better to leave it where it was and hope Liam hadn't passed any vital evidence on to it. He wasn't cut, which was a miracle, and he'd been wearing standard high-street jeans and hoody. They hadn't had a drink, they hadn't been seen, and they'd parked far enough away to not be remembered.

Liam came back into the room naked.

'Jesus.' Will ran upstairs and rifled through a wardrobe, taking care to wrap his hands in his sleeves. He found jeans and a top and ran back down. Liam's trainers weren't too bad, and he rinsed them under the tap. 'Put these on outside on the grass. Come on, get dressed.'

Liam did as he was told and they went out the way they'd come in, careful not to touch anything. Liam put his stained trainers on, then they walked to the car and got in, checking the road to make sure no one was about. Will followed the line of sight from Ormond's house and satisfied himself that they hadn't been seen.

Then he drove away.

Chapter 48

Sharon Bradley spearheaded the march out of Penrith and north along the A6 towards the Cumbria Constabulary HQ. Millie held her hand, and on his daughter's other side, Thomas kept his eyes peeled for trouble. If he couldn't protect her at home, then he wasn't letting her out of his sight.

As the day wore on, he became more tempted to report Jordan missing. Millie didn't want him to because she thought it might get him into even more trouble than he was already in. It was a dilemma that he wished Ella could help him with. He'd lost his anchor: the only person in the world who knew instinctively what to do when faced with a quandary concerning their children. He'd taken her for granted and allowed her to make the decisions, so now he was unprepared and amateur. He had no idea how to advise his daughter or discipline his son. His admiration for Ella extended beyond her qualities as a beautiful person; indeed, it was boundless. The strength, commitment, wisdom and poise necessary to nurture and encourage two other human beings was something he was only just beginning to appreciate.

Ella would have known what to do with Millie as she fled their home in search of answers he'd failed on. She'd know how to find their son. After that first glimpse of

Jordan on the TV, he had had no further sightings, and neither had Millie, but they were both convinced he was hanging around the estate. Deep in his gut, Thomas knew that Jordan wanted revenge in his own style, and part of him wanted the same. But the thought of his son going to prison for the rest of his life for first-degree murder was unbearable, and he pushed it to the back of his mind every time it raised its ugly head, concentrating on Millie instead.

The policewoman was doing her best to find him as well: all units in Penrith had been told to watch out for him. Ella had known her son's capacity for love, but Thomas saw his scope for remorselessness. That stillness, resolve and depth was something he recognised in himself; it had made him a ruthless businessman, retiring before fifty and living off his hard work. Jordan had the same steel in his eyes, and Thomas knew that whatever mission he was on, it would take heaven and earth to budge him.

For now, all he could do to revere the memory of his dead wife was to keep her daughter safe. He listened to the chanting as he marched, heard Sharon shouting about social justice and inequality. Three days ago, Thomas would have said she was missing the point. In a capitalist society, competition and inequality were key. In the survival of the fittest, some animals were caught and eaten. It was life. That was all.

But now, he admired the woman leading the peaceful protest, and he knew that Ella would have done too.

'No more knife crime!' they chanted, repeating the chorus as they made their way past stationary traffic. People got out of cars and took videos to post online, reporters clamoured for the best shots of the front of the march, and Millie squeezed Thomas's hand. She bellowed along with them and car horns tooted in support.

The mood was buoyant and lively, but suddenly the atmosphere began to change and Thomas felt pressure from behind. He held onto Millie as she looked over her shoulder. They were close to police HQ. In the distance, they saw a stationary line of police cars, and Sharon began to slow down and encourage the human train to grind to a halt. The message was passed back, and before long, the whole convoy had come to a standstill. A man squeezed through the crowd and told her that she was welcome to stand on his car to address her audience.

Thomas went to help her up, taking Millie with him. Millie gazed at Sharon in anticipation, but Thomas was busy looking around him, working out the best way to get her out of here quickly should they need to. He felt that things were about to change.

'Why are they blocking our way?' Sharon raged. The crowd roared. Thomas reckoned there were over a thousand people listening to her. He saw movement near the police cars, and officers wearing riot clothes moved across the road in front of their blockade of vehicles.

'Millie!' he said firmly. He'd managed to hold her slightly away from the car on which Sharon stood. She ignored him and pulled away.

'Why will they not speak to us?' Sharon implored. The crowd rumbled its response.

From nowhere, a missile hit the ground and smashed. The crowd parted, and for a second, people didn't know what to do. Cameras whirred, journalists shouted, children screamed. Another missile hit, and this time it made contact with a child's head, causing them to wail.

Sharon appealed for calm. Thomas had no idea where the sudden violence had come from, but it wasn't from the police.

'Don't allow yourselves to be tricked! Stop!' she pleaded.

A bottle hit her in the stomach and she bent over, winded and in shock. Before anyone could catch her, she'd fallen off the car bonnet and crashed to the ground with a thump. Thomas grabbed Millie and dragged her away from the scene, which was deteriorating quicker than he'd imagined possible. He turned back for Sharon, but she was surrounded by people trying to help.

'Dad!' Millie struggled to get to Sharon too, but she wasn't strong enough. Thomas pulled her behind a house to safety, and held her tight. She stopped wriggling and they sat down on the patch of grass behind the house, not caring who it belonged to.

Police sirens mingled with screams, and Thomas covered Millie's head and held her close to him. A woman came out of the back of the house wielding a broom, threatening to knock the living daylights out of the pair of them, until she saw Millie's terrified face. Thomas explained that they were innocently caught up in the trouble going on in the road, and the woman quickly ushered them inside and locked the back door.

They could hear the noise of pure wrath now, to the front of the house. Thomas left Millie with the woman, who'd taken it upon herself to hug her, and moved towards the window, peering through the closed curtains. The scene was one of carnage. Abandoned banners littered the road, people lay injured, police holding riot shields hit anyone in their path, knocking some of them senseless. Blood splattered on cars, smoke billowed from engines and children ran around rootless and terrified. He knew he had to do something.

His first instinct was to call 999, but he saw the fool-ishness in that as fast as it had come to him. He asked the woman if he could open her front door to see if he could get some of the casualties inside. She nodded.

'No, Dad!' Millie screeched.

He ignored her and ran to the front door. 'In here!'

A few people were cowering in the front garden and they ran inside to safety. Others saw him but were inca-pacitated or trapped on the wrong side of the police line. He made eye contact with an officer in riot gear, about to whack a woman over the head, and had an idea.

Of course! He slammed the door and ran upstairs. In the front bedroom, he took out his phone and opened the curtains far enough to film what was going on. He panned to the police blockade and saw that they were dragging people into vans. Many of them were young males, and a few took a kick to the guts as they were forced into the vehicles. He zoomed in as much as he could. He had several lawyer friends who might be interested in the footage when the day was over and the general public saw how disgracefully their police force had acted.

He was angry. Part of it was the unprovoked nature of the violent response. Part of it was that Millie and Sharon were right: there was no justice for those who refused to go quietly. The march had been peaceful, but now he re-examined his instinct that, as they neared police headquarters, the mood had changed. He panned left and filmed the last people running away, but he also caught sight of groups of people he hadn't seen before, either at the barricades, in the park before the march, or during it. They looked like hired thugs.

He zoomed in and realised that one of them was carrying a knife. He felt his palms go sweaty and his stomach tense. The youth was walking towards a police officer.

Thomas forgot the phone and shouted to warn the officer, but his voice came from behind a closed window and went unheard. Then he realised with sickening clarity what he had to do. He held up his phone once more and focused on the man walking with intent. A colleague had spotted him, but it was too late and the blade made contact in the officer's armpit, exactly where he wore no armour. Within seconds, the attacker was surrounded and apprehended on the ground, but Thomas could only stare at the officer, who lay unmoving, a pool of blood spreading out beneath him.

His hands shook and sweat was running into his eyes, but he kept filming. That was when he saw something that made his stomach hit the floor. He dropped the phone and sprinted downstairs and out of the house, running straight past the commotion on the ground as the attacker was overwhelmed, chasing after the gang of men who'd been with him.

He daren't shout his name, but Jordan turned and saw him. Thomas stopped running and bent over, leaning on his knees, but with his head up, staring after his son, who turned again and stuck up his thumb. It was brief and went unnoticed by anyone else, but Thomas knew Jordan was telling him not to worry.

It only confirmed his worst fears.

Chapter 49

Rob drove around the Lake District while Kelly spoke to the counter-corruption unit, with Jackson and Tyrone sitting in the back. She didn't want to let them out of her sight.

It was a long call, and she didn't know if she was safe going back to Eden House. At this point, she had no idea who she could trust outside her own small team, and that didn't include Will. But then he'd told her himself that he was no longer a part of her team. It hurt.

She'd called Emma first to update her. 'You might want to go home.'

Emma understood. They were at a turning point, with no way back, and she wouldn't know how to handle the counter-corruption unit.

'They have ways of getting information that you don't see coming,' Kelly told her. 'You could compromise yourself without realising it. We'll all have to be interviewed at some point; until then, the investigating team will be suspended, including Ormond, and we have no idea what he has up his sleeve. So you might as well go home. We've got our evidence; it's just a case of arresting the Cotton brothers now, and all units are looking for them.'

'All right, boss, if you're sure?'

She was.

The phone call to Counter-Corruption lasted an hour. They were serious allegations, and needed to be thoroughly investigated. Pending any decisions, Kelly and her team would have access to Eden House only for interview. Kelly had seen the unit in action once before, at the Met, and they left nothing to chance. She knew her offices would be taken over by an impartial team, who would not care what was said: they looked only at facts. It was an unpleasant business and no one wanted to be a part of it, but she was left with no choice. She had to hold her nerve, armed with the knowledge that she'd done everything correctly. She might never know what Ormond's defence would be, but she had no control over that. She had to believe that the truth would win in the end.

She heard a phone ring in the back and cocked one ear when Jackson answered.

Rob had driven down the east side of Derwent Water, past the jetties to the south and back up the west side, flanking Cat Bells. The lads had been quiet in the back, and Kelly wondered if they'd ever been over this way and knew how beautiful it was.

Finally her call was done and she rubbed her eyes, exhausted. Jackson too hung up.

'That was Jason Cotton.'

Kelly spun around. 'What did he say?'

'He wants to offer me a deal.'

'Is he crazy? Do you think it's a trap? Surely he'll know you've been talking to us?'

'Not necessarily. Sharon wouldn't grass, and everybody else has been focused on the protests.'

'What sort of deal?'

'To get the two hundred K. Working together, me and him.'

'What about his brother?'

'He said he was cutting him loose.'

'It sounds like a trap to me,' Rob said.

'Me too, brah,' said Tyrone.

'He's vulnerable and desperate. I can hear it in his voice. There are so many people who are lining up to be his opposition, and he knows he's done. He's gonna split but thinks he has a chance at the money first, if I help him.'

'But why would you?'

'I've always done shit on time, no worries, no sides, no beef.'

'Beef?'

'Trouble. They have enemies in Manchester, Preston, Wigan; you name it. Any one of them could have set Jason up. He trusts no one right now.'

'That includes you.'

'Maybe, but I don't intend on going there alone.'

'He gave you an address?'

Jackson nodded.

This created a huge problem for Kelly. It should be rung in. Armed Response would be needed. However, to get that, she'd have to go through HQ, and Ormond. She thought quickly.

'Where is it?'

Jackson told her, and she called HQ, asking for Ormond but praying he wasn't there.

'Sorry, ma'am, the super called this morning and requested urgent annual leave: a personal matter. He said he wasn't to be disturbed under any circumstances.'

'I need clearance for the armed response unit. I've been given information as to the whereabouts of the two prime suspects in the Watson and Bradley murders.'

'Right, ma'am, give me a minute.'

The operator put Kelly on hold. While she waited, she told Rob what Ormond had done.

'Interesting. Game over?'

'Let's hope so.'

Approval was given for a raid on the address with ARU backup. A tactical unit, supported by the ARU, would go in first. It was standard procedure, and Kelly was given the details of the ARU commander on duty. Now that the job was generated, there was no way back. Technically, she'd just been told by Counter-Corruption that her team was suspended, but that wouldn't come into place in reality until they moved into her office. She couldn't let this go.

'Shit, man.' Tyrone spoke from the back seat.

'What is it?' Kelly asked.

'Look.' He showed her a YouTube video: the march to police HQ had turned violent, and the clip had gone viral.

'What the hell?'

She watched the footage again and clicked on other videos, including one showing an attack on a policeman. It must have been recent, because videos like that were usually removed fairly rapidly.

'Jesus. Let's get back to Penrith. Use blues; the RV is Tactical HQ near the castle.'

The police tactical unit was trained to deal with all situations faced by police involving some kind of threat elevated above normal levels. Kelly was due to meet the ARU there so she could coordinate with the tactical unit

314

for the duration of the raid. She was still the SIO, and this was her call, but tactical command could make suggestions. She had a positive relationship with all the tactical and armed response officers she'd worked with. They all wanted the same thing: to apprehend suspects without anyone getting hurt. It would be their job to clear the warehouse and secure the perimeter before the detectives went in.

She called Johnny, who didn't answer. She had to try and keep her nerve and trust that he would have seen trouble coming and got everyone to safety. But Ted was physically weaker than the others, and it looked like it had happened very quickly. The videos showed hundreds of people running, seemingly caught off guard. Even Johnny might not have been prepared. She bit her lip and tried his number again; he still didn't pick up.

'The police officer's dead.' Tyrone read out breaking news as they sped through villages at high speed, with cars, lorries and caravans pulling over to let them past.

It was awful news, and sobering. A testimony to the anarchy created by Ormond's selfishness and greed. Kelly had told the counter-corruption unit about the Preston depot cache, and knew that, as a matter of course, Ormond's bank accounts would be scrutinised.

There was more footage being posted by the minute, and Tyrone showed Kelly the video of Sharon falling off a car. Where were Thomas and Millie? There was still no message from Ted, Johnny, Josie or Callum.

They reached the tactical unit HQ, and Kelly went inside. Rob waited in the car with Jackson and Tyrone. When she came out again, she nodded and got back into the vehicle.

'I've called Sharon, she's OK. She's back at her flat.' She turned to Jackson and Tyrone. 'We'll take you there and drop you. Don't leave.'

'Why can't we come with you?' Jackson asked.

'You know the answer to that: this is a police raid and you're civilians. It's not safe, and it's not procedure.'

'Cuz your procedure has got you so far, ain't it?' Tyrone spoke up and everyone was shocked at his confidence, Jackson was the one who did the talking. Kelly dropped her head: he had a good point.

'Alright. Let's go,' Kelly said. They watched as two armed response vehicles made ready and gave the thumbs-up.

The Beacon Estate was quiet, with many people presumably still making their way home from the disastrous march. Poor Sharon, this was a terrible outcome for her. Kelly had been surprised when she'd answered her phone. She was ripping and raging, and still the immovable force that the estate had come to love. She told Kelly that it wasn't the police who were to blame for things getting out of hand, but thugs looking for trouble who'd turned something quite beautiful into murderous panic. Only then had the police turned violent, as captured by so many people on their phones. She didn't know what had happened to Thomas and Millie.

The darkening sky enveloped them. It was only four o'clock in the afternoon, but already night had settled in.

The warehouse was situated in wasteland adjacent to the estate, and they had to drive the long way around due to the barricades at the centre. The radio crackled intermittently as Kelly finalised details with the tactical and armed response commanders. Jackson and Tyrone were silent in the back, still reeling from the coolest thing they'd experienced in a long time: a ride in a police car with blue flashing lights, clocking ninety in the lanes, and they weren't even under arrest. They sat transfixed, listening to the exchanges and checks between vehicles.

They'd been warned to stay inside the vehicle at all times and not do anything stupid.

Chapter 50

Johnny sat in the Penrith and Lakes Hospital, holding his daughter's hand. In the panic, he'd dropped his phone, or it had been knocked out of his grasp. He didn't know which. He blamed himself. He hadn't seen it coming. Nobody had.

As they'd followed the protesters out of Potton Park, the mood had been light and cheerful. Musicians played and the crowds walked happily, waving at the cameras and taking their own video clips to post online. Some walked more quickly than others, and Johnny found his small group quite close to the front as they neared police HQ. A squeeze concertinaed the crowd and he thought they'd be crushed. He warned Ted, who grabbed Josie, who held on to Callum. But they were split up.

Johnny, Josie and Callum desperately called for Ted, who they last saw going in the wrong direction. Johnny knew they were in trouble when the first missile was thrown. They watched Sharon climb onto the car and witnessed her being attacked and falling off. Johnny ushered Callum and Josie to a gateway leading to a field and shouted for people to follow him.

Satisfied that the two youngsters were safe, he told them not to move and went to find Ted.

As he ran through the crowds rushing the other way, he spotted men with hoodies and face masks throwing bottles, bits of wood ripped off gates and anything else that might cause harm. He frantically scanned the scene and worked out that most people were running in the direction of the police because they thought they'd be safe. In his experience of riot control, they would be gravely disappointed. Anyone who didn't scarper from a violent scene would instantly be viewed as an aggressor. The whole point of riot control was that force was met with greater force and things were brought rapidly to an end.

As the mass of people surged this way and that, he spotted Ted lying on a grass verge beside the road. He wasn't moving. He ran to him and went for his phone, and that was when he noticed he didn't have it. He grabbed the nearest person and ordered them to call an ambulance.

'Already did, mate, they're on their way.'

Johnny felt Ted's forehead. It was cool but not dead cold. Next he checked his pulse: it was too slow. But he heard a groan and watched as Ted opened his eyes and winced in pain. He'd just been knocked out, thank God.

'Ted?'

'Johnny? What happened?'

'I have no idea. Everything has gone wrong; it's a riot. Come on, we don't want to get caught up in it. Can you sit up?'

Ted was clearly in pain, but he tried his best and Johnny helped him to his feet. As soon as he was upright, he bent over and vomited.

'I think I'm concussed.'

'We need to get you to hospital, come on. Josie and Callum are in the field.'

'Are they OK?'

'Yes.' He helped Ted across the road. The fight was now moving in the other direction, and they watched as the police gradually gained the upper hand. Johnny shook his head: it was all so senseless. As they entered the field, Josie ran to Ted and hugged him. She sat by his side the whole time they waited. Eventually four ambulances turned up and medics treated the most serious casualties. Ted said he could wait.

Another ambulance drove directly into the field and a few people who were mildly injured approached it. Because Ted had suffered a head injury, and he told them that he had vomited, he was told he had to go to hospital. Josie sobbed as she let him go.

It was a long walk back to Johnny's car in Penrith. Josie and Callum's phones were both out of charge, and they didn't pass one pay phone that was working. By the time they reached the car, it was four o'clock and they were freezing. Johnny could barely move his hands, and he put the heaters on high. Thank God he hadn't lost his car keys.

At the hospital, they were told that Ted had been admitted, and that until he was stabilised, he couldn't have visitors.

'Stabilised?'

'Are you related to Mr Wallis?'

'He's my father-in-law.'

Josie looked at her dad but said nothing.

'He took a turn for the worse and they're working on him now. There's a waiting area on the fourth floor, near the ICU, or the restaurant is nice and warm; it's on the mezzanine.'

'Thank you. Is there a phone I could use?'

He called Kelly from a pay phone near the restaurant, but her phone went straight to voicemail.

Chapter 51

Jordan now knew what they'd been given by the police officer he recognised as Will: cash. In return for the address where Adam and Jason Cotton were hiding. He'd casually asked about the encounter, and the two men had bragged about their gains and how easy it was to get cash out of the pigs.

'Everyone knows where they are anyway, just nobody told the cops, innit.'

Jordan had laughed along with everyone else.

'They're fucked, man. They had it coming.' The young man who spoke had got away from Adam Cotton back at the warehouse. He was proud of himself, and the others thought him hard and gutsy.

Jordan had slipped away at his next opportunity. The two guys had given Will the information a couple of hours ago, so the chances were the place had been raided by now, but he had to make sure. He began walking.

Seeing his father had provoked a mixture of emotions inside him. He'd wanted to stop and go to him, check if he was all right. He felt mean making his dad chase him so far. That was why he'd stuck his thumb up.

But he couldn't go back now. If he did, his father would try and talk him into giving up his plan, with the law-abiding drivel that had got their mother killed. She'd done everything right, and look what happened to her.

He had to hold onto his anger, to make sure he didn't lose his edge. When the time came, he'd need it. The inevitable backlash – and the pain that would come with it – didn't bother him; it was more how Millie would get on without him. Dad would cope. He coped with everything in his self-flagellating manner, almost religious in his stoicism. Dad would wear a brave face his whole life, but Millie was a different beast: she was a bag of emotions and she felt everything keenly. He'd thought long and hard about how his actions might affect her, but had reached the conclusion that Millie was an individual and shit happened in life. Nothing – absolutely fuck all – was guaranteed, and everybody had crushing bad news to deal with on a daily basis somewhere on this sorry planet they were stuck on.

His head hurt with philosophy. The time for thinking was over.

He had a vague idea that he knew how to get to the address. It was some warehouse on the edge of the estate. He went alone, unafraid and confident. Hatred burned his blood.

The afternoon was getting darker by the second, and he pushed his hands into his pockets and put up his hood. No one paid him any attention as he navigated his way to the other side of the estate. He doubled back on himself several times and went round the houses a few times, but eventually he found it.

Now that he'd found the right area, he needed to get the warehouse lot correct. He walked underneath the treeline to the side of the road. The streets were all in darkness but he didn't want to take any chances. There seemed to be no indication that anything had happened here. Surely if there'd been a police raid, there would be flashing lights and tape everywhere?

But he remembered that his last impression of Will had been one of suspicion. What if he was bent and he hadn't called the information in? Maybe he was there in the warehouse now, warning the Cotton brothers, or making deals? All of these possibilities whirred around in his head.

Finally he found a sign pointing to the lot number he'd been given, and approached the building slowly. He tried the door at the front: it was locked, so he walked around the back and saw a light burning in an upstairs window. There was a metal stairway leading up to it. He took the stairs, staying vigilant in case anyone showed up. The place was silent, and he was pretty sure the cops hadn't been here.

He took care on the stairs, making sure he didn't make a sound and alert whoever was inside. When he reached the top, he found himself on a kind of landing, leading to a door. He tried the door and it opened. The light was coming from one of the rooms beyond. His heart pounded in his chest as he tiptoed towards it. He heard voices, and smelled weed. The interior door had a glass panel. He peered inside and saw two men: one was Adam Cotton. As the other man turned, Jordan realised it was Adam's brother, Jason and that the two were having a heated argument.

'They'll come,' said Jason.

Adam paced up and down. 'The others aren't coming back.'

'We don't need them. I told them to fuck off; it was only a matter of time before they ratted on us. As soon as Jackson gets here, we'll go.'

'We can't trust him.'

'We can.'

Jordan didn't know who they were talking about, but it was clear they were waiting for someone. He considered his options. He knew he couldn't take both of them. He had no choice but to attack them separately, maybe when one of them came out here for the toilet. It was one of three doors off the small entrance hall he found himself in. He tried the other doors and they were also open. He checked them out without switching any of the lights on. There was enough moonlight coming through the windows to work out that they were dumping rooms full of junk.

When he came back out to the entrance, he heard a car. He went to the window overlooking the landing at the top of the stairs and peered through gingerly. It was the two coppers he'd seen hand over the cash for the address. He didn't know what else to do for now apart from slip into one of the other rooms unseen. He closed the door behind him and listened to the two men coming up the metal staircase. They reached the top and made their way to the main room, banging on the door.

Jordan found that the room he was in contained several doors, and as his vision improved in the dark, he realised that one connected the storeroom to the main room. The door was ajar, and he could hear the exchanges clearly.

'Where's the rest of the party?' one of the coppers said. 'They deserted you?'

'Fuck off.'

Jordan didn't think the guests were expected, but they were known.

'Pleasure as always.'

He saw a faint glow of blue light through the window and went to check it out. Three police cars were approaching. Jesus, that was all they needed: more bent coppers. But then he saw Kelly Porter getting out of one of the vehicles and realised that this was the genuine raid turning up. He was running out of time. He made his decision.

He went back to the connecting door and brought out the two knives he'd taken from home. Then he took a deep breath and entered the main room.

'What the fuck?' Adam was the first to spot him. Jordan glanced at Will and the other police officer.

'Jordan!' Will said.

Jordan held the knives up in front of him.

'You know him?'

'Yes, Jason, he's the son of the woman your brother killed in Potton Park.'

The Cotton brothers stared at him.

'What's your plan, Jordan?' Will asked. 'Come for revenge? They're not worth it, lad, believe me, and they're going down anyway.'

Neither Jason nor Adam moved. They weren't quite sure what was going on. Jordan had definitely made the most of the element of surprise. But he didn't know what to do next. He'd just heard the police officer confirm that Adam had killed his mother.

'Jason?' Jordan addressed the other brother. Jason jutted his chin towards him. 'It wasn't you who did it?'

'No, he killed Keira,' Will said. 'They're a lovely pair, aren't they?'

'You can fucking talk, man,' Adam spat.

'Jordan, let me and Liam deal with this.'

'There are three cop cars outside,' Jordan said. 'Kelly is here.'

'Who the fuck is Kelly?' Jason demanded.

Will and the other officer looked at one another.

'Let me do it now, otherwise it'll be too late,' Jordan pleaded through gritted teeth.

'Jordan, stay calm,' Will said, and began walking towards him.

He held the knives so tightly that he thought he might snap one. The blades looked lethal and commanding. He had the power; he could decide. As Will got closer, he noticed the other copper advancing too. He was within whispering distance when he said, 'Hit the deck when they shout.' Then he moved away. Jordan understood. Jason and Adam hadn't heard the advice.

There was movement outside, and Jordan knew that if he was going to get to Adam, it had to be now. Ten seconds more and his chance would be gone.

Chapter 52

As they approached the rear of the warehouse, they noticed a car parked near the iron stairwell leading up to the only light in the building. Kelly and Rob got out and watched as the armed response team worked in silence with hand signals and gestures. Kelly touched the bonnet of the car: it was warm. Jason and Adam had recent visitors.

As the team readied itself to go in, she felt her phone go off. Damn, it was bloody awful timing, but she hoped it might be news from Johnny. It was a number she didn't recognise and she didn't answer it, but it called another three times in twenty seconds and so she pressed accept.

It *was* Johnny. 'Thank God! You answered!'

'Johnny? Where are you? I've been calling you.'

Rob gestured that it was fine for her to talk: he could keep an eye on the raid and would let her know when she was needed.

'I lost my phone. It turned into a riot.'

'I know, I've seen the footage, I've been worried sick. Are you all OK?'

'Where are you?'

'With Armed Response. It's a long story. We've found the brothers.'

'I'm at the hospital. Ted was injured, but he's stable now.'

'Oh Christ! I'll get there as soon as I can.'

'It's all right, I'm here with Josie. Just concentrate on what you're doing. I'll see you later.'

She ended the call. The team was ready to ascend the stairwell. Their weapons were off safety, and they cocked them in preparation. Kelly watched mesmerised as they took the stairs.

Before they were halfway up, there was a wail from inside, then a figure emerged on the metal balcony with its hands up.

'Armed police! Stop!'

'Will? Don't shoot. He's one of us.'

Armed Response lowered their weapons.

'You need to get in there,' Will said. 'Jordan's here. Liam tried to stop him...'

'Oh Jesus.'

Chapter 53

Jordan's mind had been made up in a split second, and he charged at Adam. But before he could get to him, the guy Will had called Liam pushed Adam out of his way. Adam fell to the floor and Liam spun around.

'Give us a knife, lad. I'll do it for you. You don't want to go to prison for the rest of your life. Your mum wouldn't want that.'

Everything was happening so fast, Jordan's head was spinning. Jason made for the door, but Will blocked him.

'Where do you think you're going?' He stood in the doorway and Jason pulled a knife.

'Come on then, lad,' Will said.

Jason charged at him, but he was no match for the policeman, who took him down with a single punch. The knife clattered to the floor and Will jumped on Jason and cuffed him.

Adam was cowering against a wall. Jordan realised he must be unarmed. If he'd been tooled up, he'd have pulled it by now.

'Don't do it, Jordan.' Will held up his hands.

'I want to cut him so bad.' Jordan didn't know where the words came from; all he could see was his mother lying in a pool of her own blood and Adam Cotton running away. 'Who else did it? Who was the other one?'

'I know you want to see him in pain,' Will said.

'Give me the knives, Jordan.' That was Liam.

Jordan moved closer and closer to Adam, who looked around frantically for options.

'Hold him, Liam,' Will said, and ran towards the door. Jason banged his head on the floor like a chained animal. Will ignored him.

Jordan looked at Liam, then to Adam, and back again.

They heard Will's voice outside, and then Kelly shouting. They were coming in.

Jordan's eyes stung with tears and he knew that Liam was almost next to him. He felt his grip on the knives loosen but held on. He couldn't see properly through the blur, but the rage in his heart hurt so bad.

It wasn't a choice. It wasn't conscious. He felt outside his own body as he witnessed it run towards Adam Cotton with the two knives in the air.

The last thing he saw was the face of his mother.

Chapter 54

The armed response team entered the room.

'Get down! Armed police!'

But the four men in the room were already on the floor. All on top of one another, except for one on his own, who was cuffed. There was some kind of scuffle going on, and a fair amount of blood. A gurgling noise could be heard coming from underneath it all, and the armed response unit shouted for the men to move away from one another.

The all clear had come over the radio, and Kelly took the stairs as fast as she could. She stopped dead in the middle of the room when she saw the scene. She looked from Will to Liam, who was being cradled by his friend; to Jason Cotton, cuffed on the floor; and then to Jordan Watson, who lay on his back, bloody hands in the air, staring at her.

Adam Cotton was in a critical condition. He was struggling to breathe. Someone shouted into a radio: 'Medic!'

Medics accompanied armed response units routinely, and it wasn't long before a team was running up the metal stairwell, carrying emergency equipment. Basic CPR was useless at this point: they needed to stop the blood flow. They compressed the wounds they found. Adam groaned.

Kelly made a rapid assessment in her head. Before any kind of crime-scene investigator was called, she had to stabilise the situation. Everybody was pumped full of adrenalin, and somebody had to make some serious decisions.

'He's a suspect, get him out of here,' she said, pointing to Jason Cotton.

'Fuck you, bitch.'

Jason was manhandled away.

'Jordan, are you hurt?' she asked.

He shook his head.

'Will?'

'Liam's cut pretty bad.'

'He's lucid, do an injury assessment!' shouted the medic working on Adam Cotton.

Will nodded, and Kelly helped him. Liam had a deep cut to his thigh; Will stripped his T-shirt off and wrapped the wound.

'Fuck, that hurts!' Liam gasped.

'You'll live,' Kelly said, going to Jordan. She knelt down and reached out to touch him. He was shaking and staring goggle-eyed at her. 'Jordan? Do you know who I am?'

He nodded.

'Good. Are you hurt?' She looked him over quickly. He shook his head.

'What happened?' he asked.

Kelly's eyes flickered over to where Adam Cotton was lying, and Jordan followed them. The young man was on his back, surrounded by officers trying to save his life. He convulsed as blood spurted out of him.

'Was that me?' Jordan asked faintly.

'You don't remember?'

He shook his head.

'No, it was me,' Liam said. 'Cotton had two knives and went for Jordan. I got in the middle.'

Kelly glanced back to where Adam Cotton lay and saw two knives on the floor close by. She knew with every fibre of her being that they belonged in Thomas Watson's knife block. There was little she could do to protect Jordan now.

'And Jordan was the target but he came out unscathed?'

'I was faster than Adam.'

Kelly stood up and looked at the two officers. She still had no clear answer for why they'd behaved as they had, and she still didn't know if she could trust Will.

'How did you find this place before me?' she asked him.

Will's expression didn't change. Kelly locked glances with Liam and his eyes never flickered. She looked back at Jordan, who looked vacant and confused.

'Informants?'

Will nodded.

'And you, Jordan. What were you doing here?'

'I worked out where they were.'

'And you came here to do what?'

'Is he under caution?' Liam asked. Kelly glared at him. 'Don't say anything, lad,' he told Jordan.

Kelly nodded. 'Jordan, I'm going to have to take you into custody until we can work out what happened here.'

'He's gone,' announced one of the medics. 'Time: four fifty-four p.m.'

Kelly looked at Will and Liam. 'I'm arresting you two as well.'

Rob entered the room, having dealt with the arrest of Jason Cotton, and looked at Will.

'Rob, take these two officers to the station, please, I'll accompany Jordan.' She looked at Will. 'Do I need cuffs?'

He shook his head.

The crime-scene team would soon arrive to start gathering evidence. No doubt the case would land on somebody's desk tonight. It wouldn't be hers. Counter-Corruption had already called and summoned her to Eden House.

It had begun.

But first she was going to see Johnny and Ted.

Chapter 55

Millie sat huddled in Sharon's flat watching TV. Her father couldn't settle and had gone to look for Jordan. He was out in the dark, walking round aimlessly. They couldn't stop him and Sharon had explained to her that he needed to do it. Besides, Millie was happy to be looked after by the woman she'd grown close to over the last twenty-four hours. Sharon had made hot chocolate.

The afternoon's violence was reported on TV, but it was interrupted by a bulletin promising breaking news.

'Police in Penrith tonight targeted an address in the city and apprehended two suspects wanted in connection with the murders of Keira Bradley and Ella Watson earlier in the week. Cumbria Constabulary have issued a statement saying that one of the men has since died of wounds sustained at the scene. We'll bring you more news as we get it.'

They stared at one another in disbelief.

'Fucking hell!' Sharon said.

Millie laughed, and it felt good. 'My mum never swore in front of me.'

'You're shitting me? How did she manage that?'

She laughed again. 'Did you always swear in front of Keira?'

Sharon looked at the TV, deep in thought. Millie thought she might have upset her, but then Sharon took her hand.

'Always! I couldn't bear the stench of her nappies, I swore every time I opened one. So will you, it's disgusting.'

'I want loads of babies.'

'Don't bother. They're not as cute as they look, you know, and all they do is shit, piss and scream. Then they turn into toddlers and scratch your eyes out, and eventually – the best bit – teenagers! Live your life instead. There are no guarantees. Travel, see the world, bed some gorgeous men.'

'Sharon!'

'What? How old are you? Fourteen? I was pregnant at your age.'

'I haven't... yet.'

'It's overrated, love, but sometimes it's nice, if you find the right one.'

'There's a boy I like, but I don't think he likes me.'

'Why?'

'He ignores me, but then he'll steal my book in biology.'

'He proper fancies you. Classic signs. What about Jordan? Does he have a girl?'

'He has loads!' Millie smiled, but then grew melancholy at the mention of her brother.

'I'm sorry, love. He'll turn up, you'll see. He's angry, and he has every right to be. If he's anything like you, he's a good egg inside. He'll know deep down not to get caught up with these bad 'uns round here. They'll ruin him.'

'That's what my dad's scared of. It's as if all the effort and money that went into bringing him up will be wasted.'

'That's a bit harsh. I wish I could give Keira what you guys have.'

'It's funny, isn't it? That you think I have everything, but I think you do. You're kind, thoughtful and friendly, and you've created this whole community that wasn't there before. We have three expensive cars, a massive house, private education and skiing lessons, and I just want to live here with you.'

'You're a darlin', you are.' Sharon reached for her cigarettes, took one out and lit it. Millie watched.

'Can I try it?' she asked.

Sharon passed her the cigarette and lit another. Millie sucked it and blew out, coughing.

Sharon laughed. 'You'll get the hang of it.'

'How's your shoulder?' Millie asked, holding onto the cigarette and watching the smoke drift upwards. Sharon had refused to go to hospital after her fall, saying she wasn't seriously hurt, but Millie had seen her wince when she went to lift something up.

There was a bang at the door, and Millie jumped. Sharon went to get up, but it was too painful and she sat back down. Millie stubbed out her cigarette.

'I'll go.'

She disappeared, and Sharon heard her open the door. 'Dad! Where's Jordan?'

Thomas closed the door but didn't reply.

They came back into the room and he greeted Sharon. Millie sat down next to her and Thomas lowered himself into a chair. He looked haggard and beaten.

'What happened?' It was Sharon who spoke. Millie held onto her arm.

'Jordan's OK. He's safe.'

'What does that mean?' Millie asked. 'Why isn't he with you?'

Thomas looked at Sharon's cigarette. 'Can I have one?'

She passed him the packet and the lighter.

'Dad, you don't smoke!'

'Your mother and I smoked before we had you and Jordan. We gave up. I've missed it every single day.'

She watched as he lit up and inhaled deeply.

'Christ, that's good.'

'There's whisky in the kitchen,' Sharon said. 'You look like you need it.'

He got up, taking his cigarette with him, and they heard him rummaging around and pouring something into a glass. He came back sipping it, then sat down and looked at them.

'He found the Cotton brothers.'

Sharon and Millie gasped.

'It was Adam Cotton and an associate of his who killed Ella – your mother. I don't know how else to say it, Millie. I'm sorry. I thought I'd feel relief at knowing, but I don't.'

Sharon squeezed Millie and the girl closed her eyes.

'But where's Jordan, Dad?'

'It turns out he's spent the last few days doing what I suspected: trying to track them down. He found them in some warehouse, but the police weren't far behind.'

'What did he do?' Millie and Sharon waited.

'It's unclear. He got into a scuffle with Adam Cotton. I don't think he intended to do it. I'm sure it was a mistake, or a flash of anger.'

'Dad!'

Thomas jumped and stared at his daughter.

'What did he do?'

'Adam Cotton is dead. He was stabbed. Kelly Porter called me and I went straight over there. Jordan's been arrested.'

Millie burst into noisy sobs. Thomas hung his head, and his shoulders sank lower as tears fell to the carpet. After a few moments, he composed himself and coughed, wiping his eyes.

'I was able to be with him throughout the whole thing. He's got a lawyer there. We're waiting to hear if he's being charged with murder.'

Chapter 56

Johnny clasped her hand.

She hated this place. The Penrith and Lakes was where her mother had died, where she went to watch autopsies, and where Ted now lay, in a critical but stable condition, having been beaten to the ground by mindless thugs getting off on the violence spilling over from events on the Beacon Estate.

She blamed Ormond. If he hadn't given the order for Op Eagle, the young men on the estate wouldn't have harboured such anger. None of the arrests from that night had given up anything useful. All it had done was alienate people further.

They sat in a waiting area on uncomfortable plastic chairs. Callum's father had picked the two teenagers up and taken them home. Josie wanted to stay but Johnny explained there was nothing they could do.

'So what will Counter-Corruption do?' he asked. He was passing time for her.

'I suppose they'll look under every rock. Everybody will be guilty until proven innocent. I won't be allowed into the office except for interview, and that goes for the whole team.'

'What about cases?'

'They'll be handed to other teams, perhaps in Lancaster, maybe in Barrow or Carlisle.'

'You'll be popular.'

'Especially at Christmas.'

'It's almost time to get a tree.'

She smiled. She knew what he was doing and she allowed herself to be distracted. Christmas was going to be tough. It was her first one without her mother. Memories of last year flooded back and she fiddled with the ring Johnny had given her. The rubies were blood red, but she'd seen so much blood over the last week that she'd become almost immune. The pool around Adam Cotton had become an oil slick for the medics and uniforms to slip around in as they'd tried to save him.

She slumped her head onto Johnny's shoulder and closed her eyes.

'What will happen to the Watson boy?'

'I don't know. I think it's quite clear what happened, but with what he's been through and Liam not budging from his story that he got in between them, it could be a surprise. He'll be dealt with in juvenile court, and he's got no previous. There are also huge mitigating circumstances.'

'We should be celebrating you cracking both cases. What happened to Ormond?'

'Counter-Corruption will find him; it's their problem now. I just hope he hasn't got a contingency plan to get him off the hook. With the solicitor's testimony, as well as the links to organised crime, I can't think of any scenarios that would save him now. I wonder if he's done a runner. He's been getting away with it for so long now that to lose it all would be devastating. How does a man like that go from king of the jungle to nothing?'

'His pride will definitely take a bashing, but people like that usually lie anyway, and go down crying their innocence. They're in permanent denial.'

Kelly saw June and Amber turn the corner and rush towards them. They both stood up and the four of them embraced, exchanging updates and answering questions.

'Can we see him?'

'Not yet. I think he should be back from his MRI and they'll have to look at it.'

'We watched the riot on TV.'

'I think a lot of people did.'

A man in a white coat walked down the corridor and smiled at them.

'This is Dad's consultant,' Kelly said. She introduced June and Amber.

'Good news,' he said. 'You father's pulling through. We're happy with the MRI scan and that the damage is temporary. He's had quite a knock but it doesn't seem to have caused a major event, just severe bruising. He's going to be in a lot of pain for a while yet. He's groggy, but he'd like to see you. If you want to follow me?'

Johnny squeezed her hand and they followed the consultant along a series of corridors. The smells, the noises and the sounds of the sick disturbed Kelly. In her job she saw the worst a human body could be put through, but she could never work in a hospital. The consultant stopped outside a private room.

'Could you keep it to around ten minutes? He needs to rest.'

'Of course.'

They went in. The room was dark, lit only by a small lamp. Ted lay propped up in the bed, his head bandaged. He turned slowly to the door and smiled at them. Kelly went to the bed and held his hand. June and Amber stood either side of her.

'Can I give you a hug?' Amber asked.

'A gentle one.' His voice was weak and Kelly was reminded of the frailty and vulnerability of the human body: they were all just an arrangement of flesh and bones that could be broken and torn. He had a black eye and the other one was bandaged.

'We haven't had a conversation about my sight, but I'm not daft. I think I'll struggle with my left.'

'You don't know that for sure,' Kelly said. 'There'll be masses of swelling; I can see it under the bandages. Just wait until all that goes down. I'm so relieved, Dad. I couldn't believe it when they told me. Do you know who it was? Did you see them?'

'No, it was a big mess and I didn't see it coming. I thought I'd fallen. I only remember Johnny helping me up.'

Johnny took his hand and shook it. 'Any time.'

'This is a happy reunion; we must do it more often!'

'Dad!' His strength was diminished but his character was indomitable.

'I know they've given you ten minutes, so come on, tell me you've cracked the cases, Kelly.'

'Have you?' asked June.

'We got them. All of them. You were right, Dad. Ella was murdered randomly, and Keira was murdered by someone who knew her. For very different reasons, but I won't bore you with that now. You need to rest.'

'I knew you'd do it.'

Kelly didn't mention the counter-corruption investigation.

'It was such a shame about the march, because the whole thing was fabulous. Why do the few always have to spoil things? Is the organiser all right? The one who fell off the car?' Ted continued.

'Yes, she is, and it's only made her more determined to carry on.'

'Good for her. I'll go to her next rally,' said Amber. 'If I'd been there, I would have knocked the blocks off those thugs.' No one in the room doubted her.

A nurse came in and apologised for the interruption but Mr Wallis needed his sleep.

'I do not! I need my family.'

The nurse smiled. 'Ten more minutes.'

They chatted for a few minutes more, all thankful for the opportunity to see Ted awake and lucid.

'My brain's obviously made of rubber.'

After saying their goodbyes, and insisting he rest — his eyes were closing anyway — they walked to the car park together and arranged to meet back at the hospital tomorrow.

Then Johnny drove Kelly to Eden House.

Chapter 57

As Mrs Ormond parked her brand-new Audi in the driveway, she noticed that Neil's car was there too. He usually spent Saturday afternoons at the golf club, at the bar, swapping stories of birdies and bogeys with his tiresome friends. Things tended to go on way into the evening and invariably he'd end up getting a cab home. So to see his car was odd. She opened the boot and carried her shopping to the front door, locking the car behind her.

Once inside, she cursed her husband for leaving a window open, because the house was bloody freezing. It was annoying; at this time of year, it was so lovely to walk into a warm house. She wondered if the back door was open, because it really was very cold.

'Neil!' she called. There was no reply, so she left the shopping in the hallway, took her shoes off and went upstairs to check.

She went from room to room in the sprawling six-bedroom home that they rattled about in these days. She was looking forward to the children coming home for Christmas. There were no windows open, so it must be downstairs.

She tutted. 'Neil!' She shouted his name one more time and gave up. She figured he must have gone outside for something and forgotten to close the door. Perhaps he was gardening. They'd neglected the weeding at the end of the season, and some plants still needed cutting back, even though the first frost had descended weeks ago now.

She heard a sound and stopped. She was at the top of the staircase and couldn't quite decide what it was, then the penny dropped and she knew that next door's dog had probably got through the fence. She heard it again: it was a whimper and a little howl.

Bless her. She must be hungry. She went downstairs and picked up the shopping, taking it through to the utility room: the back entrance to the kitchen.

'Raffles?'

The dog woofed and panted and she heard its claws scratching on the tiled floor.

'I knew it was you! I've got a treat for you!'

But the dog didn't come. Neil had probably already fed it. He was such a softie when it came to Raffles; they'd even discussed getting a dog of their own.

She opened the back door and called her husband again, walking around the house to the garden. That was when she noticed that the French doors were wide open. No wonder the house was so cold! She tutted again, and closed them, peering into the kitchen but seeing no sign of either Neil or Raffles. Maybe the dog had gone home.

She walked back to the utility room door and closed it behind her. Instantly the chill started to lift. Neil was in big trouble.

After she'd finished unpacking the shopping, she unloaded the washing machine and flicked on the radio, then went into the kitchen area, where she swore she could hear the dog again.

'Raffles?'

It was definitely the sound of a dog grooming itself, probably satisfied after a feed.

She went towards the kitchen sink and rounded the island.

Before she sank to her knees, she didn't think to scream, nor did she have time to question whether she was in some kind of dream-like state. She simply vomited, and the dog came padding over to her, the fur around its mouth all red.

Next to the cooker, on his back, lay her husband of forty years, the father of her girls. He was covered in blood and his chest seemed to have been ripped apart. His skin was almost blue, and great black patches had formed on his arms. She knew he was dead.

When her senses came back to her, one by one, she wriggled towards him and felt his face: he was stone cold.

'Neil! Neil! Help me!'

She found her voice and screamed, over and over again. She heard banging on the French windows and noticed her neighbour peering in. The dog ran to its owner, leaving a trail of bloody pawprints.

The neighbour came in, and when she saw the scene, she gagged and stepped away to dial 999.

When the ambulance arrived, the death was instantly treated like a homicide and Serious Crime was contacted.

Chapter 58

Counter-Corruption had taken over the offices on the top floor of Eden House. They hadn't wasted any time, but that wasn't surprising. Ormond was one of the top-ranking officers in the country.

Kelly walked wearily. She felt a bone tiredness akin to fatigue and knew that she was exhausted. Maybe she was coming down with something. She was shown to an interview room by a surly-looking officer in a suit who avoided eye contact. Her team were already waiting there, including Will Phillips.

'Boss,' Kate greeted her.

'How's everyone doing?' Kelly asked. They filled her in and told her that the counter-corruption officers had begun trawling through their computer files and case documents.

The door opened and Emma's name was called.

'They're going in alphabetical order,' Kate said.

The rest of them sat and listened as Kelly brought them up to date on the afternoon's events. Jordan Watson had been taken to a juvenile correction facility in Carlisle, where his father would meet him tomorrow with his lawyer. The CPS would have a decision by then as to whether there was a case to pursue against him. Liam

Brook was downstairs in one of their cells; again, the CPS would decide if he should be charged.

She glossed over the events at the warehouse but caught Will's eye several times. She couldn't help but be drawn to him, because she had such affection for him and had done for a long time. She just wanted to know the truth.

Emma didn't come back. The door opened again.

'DS Phillips, please.' Will left. After another hour, he hadn't returned either. Kelly was becoming increasingly uncomfortable, and they all filled time with calling loved ones, sorting out domestic arrangements and discussing the case.

It was usually a cause for celebration when they reached the conclusion to an inquiry, but this was different. They didn't congratulate one another, though Kelly did thank for them for their incredible hard work.

'What shall I say?' Rob asked.

'Tell the truth. We've done nothing wrong and we've got nothing to hide. That's all I ask.'

She glanced up as the door opened.

'DI Porter, please.'

She was led upstairs to her own incident room. She hardly recognised it. At least ten officers sat at desks, and she knew none of them. Nobody looked at her. They were all busy staring at screens and making copy files. It felt personal and she found herself on the defensive instantly. She was shown into her office. A woman sat at her desk and gestured for her to sit down. Another officer sat to the side with a laptop.

The preliminaries were read out: why they were there, how the process worked, how long it might take, and various legalities and housekeeping. Kelly tried not to look terrified.

'When was the last time you saw Superintendent Ormond?'

'I'm entitled to a chaperone.'

The woman running the proceedings sighed and nodded to a colleague, who went to grab a fellow officer.

'Impartial.'

The woman nodded again, and this time they went to get a uniform from the front desk. It was a familiar face, and Kelly smiled. They quickly ran through instructions for conduct and boundaries, and began again. Kelly answered the question.

'He hasn't been in the office throughout the whole inquiry. I last saw him downstairs at the Watson press conference appeal. Though he called me last night to threaten me. I think he was drunk.'

'Can I just point out that this isn't an interrogation, DI Porter. I'm simply gathering timelines and perspectives. Superintendent Ormond was found dead tonight at his home. He'd been stabbed. The CSI gave an estimated time of death between midday, when he was seen leaving his golf club, and three p.m. He was seen leaving the clubhouse in a hurry.'

'Jesus.'

'I wanted to be the one to inform you. It's become clear to us that this is an inquiry into the conduct of a lone officer. Under those circumstances, the rest of the team can operate in a quasi-skeleton capacity. I'm the SIO, and I want you on the case. Let's start at the beginning, shall we? Tell me what happened when

Superintendent Ormond was given the news about Ella Watson's death.'

Kelly took a deep breath, and began.

–

By the time she left Eden House, it was 11 p.m. The SIO expected her in the office by midday tomorrow. It meant she could have a much-needed lie-in, and go and see Ted.

She got a squad car to take her to Johnny's. He'd picked Josie up and they'd had pizza. She crept in quietly and found him asleep on the sofa with the fire still crackling and an empty glass on the table. She poured herself one and sat beside him, not wanting to disturb him. It was enough to be next to him, staring at the fire as it fizzled and popped. She got up carefully and threw another log on.

Of all the outcomes in this case, the murder of Neil Ormond wasn't something she'd ever contemplated; she'd had no reason to. She knew that Ormond's house was currently being picked over for evidence, not just for his murder, but for the corruption inquiry. Ironically, they didn't need a warrant. If there was anything to find, they'd sniff it out.

She was numb.

The murder was shocking, yes, but a man like that must have had a queue of people wanting to take him out. She tried to work out if the Cotton brothers might have had the brazen arrogance – and the time – to carry out the attack and get back to the warehouse. Of course they could have.

She closed her eyes and put her glass down. Johnny's sofa was large and soft and she grabbed a blanket from the arm and covered herself, lying down so that they topped and tailed. He murmured and sighed and she drifted into a grateful sleep.

Chapter 59

Jordan woke up in his cell. He felt at peace, which was more than he'd felt last night when he'd peered into his father's broken face. The juvenile facility was noisy and he'd slept badly, but at least he was calm. It was the first time he'd kept still since Wednesday, when his world had changed forever.

His dad's lawyer had argued last night that there wasn't enough evidence to charge him for any crime, and they'd have to release him today. Jordan simply could not remember what had happened. All he recalled was Liam pulling at him, and crawling away from Adam's body.

'They'll have to prove that you put the blade into him, and with Liam Brook confessing that he did it, they'll have a hard time forming a case.'

'I wish I had done it,' he'd said.

'Jordan!' His father had broken down.

'There's no shame here, Jordan. Any jury will be sympathetic to the strain you've been under, and it's been a very public strain.'

'I wanted to kill him. He confessed to killing my mother.'

'Think about Millie when you say that.'

Jordan could have reached out and strangled his father for using brazen blackmail, but it worked. The death of

354

Adam Cotton was redemption; further torturing Millie would be utterly selfish and unnecessary. He had no care for his own skin: he would let the law decide.

The lawyer explained that the Crown would have to prove beyond reasonable doubt that he was in sound mind after the brutal murder of his mother and had planned the execution for some time. 'Brook's confession provides reasonable doubt, as well as your memory loss due to PTSD.'

'But I'd brought two knives along; doesn't that look a bit suspicious?'

'You were alone and confused, and bravado fed your desperate need for attention after the loss of your mother.'

It was bullshit, but Jordan could see where the lawyer was going with it.

'Adam Cotton was a lowlife murderer and drug dealer, while you're a high-achieving, law-abiding boy who lost his mother, in a very public manner, four days ago.'

'And that makes it OK?'

'This is about not further splintering your family when it has been through enough. If you were charged – and I doubt you will be, because the CPS tends to stay clear when there is reasonable doubt – no juror would want to feel responsible for putting you away when another Adam Cotton somewhere else could randomly stab an innocent woman to death.'

'What about Jason?'

'He's broken under interrogation and confessed to the other murder, saying that Adam was instructed to kill a second woman to draw attention away from the real target: Keira Bradley.'

Thomas winced and hung his head. The lawyer put his hand on his shoulder.

'I'm sorry, Tom.'

'Mum was collateral damage,' said Jordan.

'Jason is looking at life for murder. As is Adam Cotton's accomplice.'

Thomas had been shown photos of the second man responsible for his wife's murder and he was merely a boy. It was heartbreaking. His defence was that he was high on ketamine at the time.

'It turns out that the Beacon Estate has been in the pocket of a high-ranking police officer, who, incidentally, was stabbed to death in his own home yesterday.'

Thomas raised his brow and wondered if Neil Ormond knew who it was. 'It looks like Ella exposed something rotten and left us all a legacy.' The lawyer patted Thomas on the back; he was an old friend and they went back years.

Thomas nodded: it was a bitter recompense.

'Did you pay the reward, Dad?'

'No one came forward, and it was DI Porter who cracked the case in the end, with dogged attention to detail. But I've got an idea what to do with the money.'

'I think you should keep it to yourself, Tom,' said the lawyer.

'I disagree. That estate pulled together, and Sharon Bradley got people to do what they would never normally do, for her daughter and for Ella.'

Jordan put his head in his hands and began to sob, deep, heavy grunts. Thomas went around the table and took his son in his arms until he was spent.

'I understand why you wanted to do it, son.'

'I'm sorry, Dad.'

'No. Don't say that. It wasn't your fault. None of this was your fault.'

Chapter 60

One month later

A cheer went up as Kelly carried the fifteen-pound turkey to the table. They were all gathered in her house, and the fire roared.

Kelly's Christmas gift to Josie was being put to good use as they pitted their wits against Thomas and Millie. It was a board game called Talisman, which challenged players to a titanic battle of magic and evil, set against an epic journey to the inner kingdom, where one player would take the Tower of Command and rule over all others. They'd been playing for three hours and still hadn't got close to the ultimate prize. The table had been set up buffet style to cater for so many people.

Kate had popped in with some bubbly, and Rob and Mia showed off their new baby. He was passed around like a parcel, and enjoyed the attention from June and Amber. June had supplied six boxes of her beautiful chocolates for the spread. Kelly couldn't help but notice how tired and harassed Mia looked, as if she hadn't had a decent night's sleep. Rob told her it was incessant.

Ted was able to walk now and refused to use the wheelchair provided by the hospital. Further checks were required on his left eye, and for now, he was unable to work. He took a bow in his apron and was grateful to be kept busy helping Kelly with the food.

Kelly had felt off colour for some time now, and was trying to shake a virus, picked up no doubt after the stress of the corruption inquiry. Her fears that she'd be shut off from the investigation were unfounded. She'd been regularly updated once her team had been indisputably cleared. USBs recovered from Ormond's property revealed that remnants of Tombday's wealth still languished in the Isle of Man, and he had been siphoning off chunks of it. Video footage had also been seized recording boys being abused by men associated with the racket. Identification would likely never be made, given that the material appeared to be twenty years old. Despite a thorough investigation into Ormond's murder, the case remained unsolved, to the desperate anguish of his family.

Sharon walked around with a bottle of sherry and topped up glasses, humming Christmas songs to herself and blowing the odd party trumpet, popped out of crackers bought at the market in Penrith. Occasionally she'd sneak up behind whoever held the baby and peer around, surprising him with a silly face.

Kelly went back into the kitchen with Ted and counted out the cutlery. Johnny was showing Jackson how to make lump-free gravy: a speciality of his, and a skill that would come in handy when the new Hub opened in early Spring.

The Ella Watson and Keira Bradley Foundation was to launch on the site of the old barricade on the Beacon Estate, and would welcome the whole community. It had received funding to offer educational and vocational courses, and would have a permanent member of staff giving advice on social and financial matters; but most importantly of all, it would be somewhere for people to go who felt disconnected from their community. The launch would celebrate the knife amnesty organised by Jackson, which had yielded one hundred and twenty-three weapons in a week. Hot and cold food would be available, as well as sports and games. The foundation would be run by Sharon Bradley and Jackson Akers, with Thomas Watson in charge of the finances.

Thomas's two hundred thousand pounds was funding the building, but he was also paying for a brand-new music suite with a recording studio after finding out about Jackson's talent. Until it was ready, Thomas had arranged for Jackson to record his music in a suite in Kendal, and his first track was available on YouTube and currently climbing the charts. His artist name was Gunz. KSI's agent had expressed an interest in working with him. The Hub was to be officially opened by two *Coronation Street* stars.

Kelly glanced around her home and noticed that Jordan had gone out onto the terrace. She slipped out to join him. The food was almost ready.

'Hey. You OK?' she asked.

He nodded. 'I'm just thinking about Mum.' He was staring at the hills.

'She liked to run up there?'

He nodded again. 'She'd have been really happy today. She loved doing things like this.'

Kelly leant on the fence next to him and gazed up at the hills where she loved to run too.

'Lunch is nearly ready.' She touched his back tenderly and walked back inside.

Under juvenile court, with no previous, and mitigating circumstances, a judge had ruled that Jordan had to wear a tag for six months. Liam Brook was facing trial for manslaughter, and had been released on bail.

Kelly missed Will. The investigation into Ormond hadn't unearthed any links back to serving personnel, only code names. But Will had decided to take a secondment to Lyon, France, to work with Interpol. Before he'd gone, she'd given him an old VHS tape. It was the only time she'd ever taken physical evidence for her own purposes. But she was sure. When you worked with someone every day for three years, and you knew the way they moved, the way they stared and the way they sat still, it never left you. She knew that one of the boys on the tape was him. That was the hold that Ormond had had over him.

Ted announced that they were almost ready. The table groaned under the weight of the food. Kelly sat down in front of the fire. She didn't much fancy eating, and even the glass of red she cradled wasn't going down well. She knew she could easily be forgiven for being a little off, given that last year, Wendy had gone into a seizure on this very sofa and never left hospital.

But she knew that wasn't the whole story.

This morning, she'd gone to find Johnny on the terrace, her face as white as the snow covering the distant mountains, and given him a small plastic stick. On it, inside a window, was a little blue cross.

'I'm pregnant,' she'd said.

Acknowledgements

I would like to thank the following people for their continued support of the Kelly Porter series.

At Canelo, Louise, Fran and the whole team; your energy and passion for the series is fantastic. From the first manuscript to the final edit, you're with me every step.

To my agent, Peter Buckman, for your advice, patience and faith.

To my children, Tilly and Freddie, who straightened out my street language to their exacting standards, and to their friends, who helped with the lyrics.

Calm.

Thank you to Dave Part, my old friend, who first flagged up the shocking young offending statistics to me. I hope Barb approves x

To the lemons, limes and pips for endless conversations about murder. Billy, I will not make you a deranged killer…

And Mike, my biggest supporter and the person who picks me up and dusts me off… I love you.

Finally, I want to dedicate this book to all the young people who have senselessly died as a result of knife crime. It should not be happening.